MW00333893

The Big 11+
VOCABULARY
PLAY BOOK
Pathway to Success

The Armadillo's Pillow Ltd.

Copyright © 2018 The Armadillo's Pillow Ltd.
All rights reserved.

This book may be photocopied, for use in schools or the pupil for which it was purchased, but may not be reproduced in any other form without the prior permission in writing from the publishers.

ISBN-13: 978-1-912936-01-4

71-75 Shelton Street
Covent Garden
London, England, WC2H 9JQ
United Kingdom

PATHWAY TO SUCCESS
Expanding your vocabulary

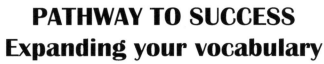

In preparation for standardised tests, such as the Eleven Plus CEM exam (Durham University's Centre for Education and Monitoring), GL Assessment (known as NFER), Common Entrance examinations and Year 6 SATs, it is essential that children have the broadest vocabulary possible.

With a strong vocabulary, students are better equipped to deal with text comprehension, identifying synonyms and antonyms, cloze testing, and other forms of verbal reasoning.

It is widely accepted that the easiest way to memorise any new material is by enjoying the learning involved. However, achieving an Eleven Plus level of vocabulary has often been an onerous task with emphasis placed on just a few types of study, chief of these being the ubiquitous stack of flash cards, word lists, and monotonous workbooks.

The best way to develop a dynamic vocabulary – a wonderful and useful tool regardless of exams – is to read extensively. I recommend this above all else. However, to reach examination standard in a shorter timeframe, this book offers a diverse selection of word challenges tailored to adhere to the requirements of the Eleven Plus.

The goal of these photocopiable materials is to give your child fun activities that will greatly improve their ability to retain new vocabulary. It can also be useful beyond the day of the exam and enable you to know that whatever the result, the learning period will have been time well spent.

Many traditional pencil and paper games, puzzles and word challenges are included. Note that a full list of the vocabulary used in this book, as well as an answer key have been included.

Go ahead. Have fun.

Elizabeth Judge
The Armadillo's Pillow Ltd

HOW TO USE THIS BOOK

ALL YOU NEED:
Pencils, scissors, dice, and occasionally, a little glue (or tape, if you will)

This book is about learning and effectively memorising, it is not about testing what is not yet learnt.

That being the case, there is no cheating; the glossary and answer pages are intended to help, and looking up words is encouraged.

The book provides 52 different activities ideally arranged to provide a new activity each week. They may be used in any order, with the exception of *Noughts and Crosses*, as this is designed for revision close to the exam.

We all have busy lives. If you are aware that your child has a particularly full week ahead, we recommend that you pick an activity marked SHORTER. Likewise, we suggest that activities marked LONGER are most suitable for the weekends or school holidays (although none of these activities are so long that they could not be completed in an evening).

Using this book, your child can expect to learn 20 new words each week without it becoming a chore. As they learn, they will 'magically' come across words in their reading and everyday life that before they had not noticed, skipped over through lack of understanding, or simply misinterpreted. Now is the time to advise your child to use this vocabulary as often as possible.

You will notice that some vocabulary is repeated and some activities have more words than others. This is to refresh and provide thematic links that will support learning.

Encourage your child to use the pages at the back of the book to practise new words. There is no need to be boring — maybe they like to use bubble writing, create a border of synonyms, make up funny sentences or draw pictures of words. These are all effective ways of learning.

The opportunity to photocopy allows your child to revisit the vocabulary through games and puzzles as often as they wish.

Contents

Contents

WORD SEARCH

First, find the synonyms of the words below by matching them with the words that most closely match them in the word bank. Next, look for the synonyms in the word search on the opposite page. Words may be in the puzzle forwards or backwards, diagonally or vertically.

SYNONYM

CHEAT   _____

PERSUADE   _____

GAIN   _____

UNIMPORTANT   _____

UGLY   _____

HIDE   _____

MAYHEM   _____

WELL BUILT   _____

MODEST   _____

SMALLER NUMBER   _____

JOKER   _____

A LIST FOR TAKING TURNS   _____

BLACK   _____

PEACEFUL   _____

A PIG'S FOOT   _____

LUXURIOUS   _____

AN UNMARRIED LADY   _____

RASCAL   _____

UNLUCKY   _____

WORD BANK

GROTESQUE	KNAVE	LAVISH	CHAOS	BENEFIT	JESTER
CURSED	HUMBLE	ROTA	SPINSTER	COAX	EBONY
TRIVIAL	SHROUD	SWINDLE	STURDY	TROTTER	
MINORITY	TRANQUIL				

WORD SEARCH

```
O N P B L A I V I R T W Y T
A S E L A Y J E S T E R T O
F N T M L D T X V I P T I M
L O D E S R U C Q F M R R R
R A E O N U O U O E A O O F
S P I N S T E R D N L T N N
L I S I X S A L O E A T I E
B I A F Q U O T L B M E M U
S H U M B L E N I V Q R L Q
D W E Q A P L X A O C D O S
U C I O N I S O K E U S V E
O N G N L A T I L N O S P T
R A N O D U R W S A A Z C O
H S I V A L E T H T E V T R
S M Y N O B E C A F J I E G
```

WANTED

You are a police illustrator. Can you create a WANTED poster, using all of the descriptive evidence you have been given?

shifty – wearing a beret – lofty – unkempt – wearing overalls – wearing galoshes – bulbous nose – an elliptical-shaped face – with horn-rimmed spectacles – grimace – matted beard

WHERE AM I?

Find the **grid location** of these images hidden in the picture on the following pages, writing the grid numbers next to each word:. Be careful, some of the pictures do not have a word!

HELIX	FLOTILLA
FOLIAGE	TENT WITH AN AWNING
FELINE	PEAK
PACHYDERM	FOUNDRY
AMPHIBIAN	CREEK
FORT	HADDOCK
MANOR	IMP
MACE	SOMBRERO
BOVINE	CONSTABLE
CANINE	STALLION
CHEVRON	

<u>BONUS</u>: Can you find the **dromedary**?

SNAKES AND LADDERS

Play the game in the traditional manner, with each player throwing the dice in turn, moving forward the corresponding number of squares along and up the board.

Usually landing on the bottom of the ladder means that you move up the ladder to the top. Alternately if you land on a square with the snake's head you slip down to the square where the snake's tail ends.

In this version, before beginning, cut out the snake and ladder cards and place them in two piles. If you land at the bottom of a <u>ladder</u>, you must answer a ladder card first. To do this, you must provide an **antonym** for the word in capitals (a possible answer is provided on the back). If successful, then the player may climb to the top of the ladder. If they incorrectly answer, they must stay in the square they landed on, and will have to roll the dice to move on their next turn.

If you land on square with a <u>snake</u>'s head, then you do not automatically slide down. You can save your position by correctly providing a **synonym** to the word given in capitals on one of the snake cards.

Ladder Card = Antonym

Snake Card = Synonym

Note: You may have an equally good answer as the one on the back of the card. Use your good judgement to decide if it is indeed a good match. To win you must reach the 100 number square before any other player.

The game board, and cards are provided on the next pages.

 MALICE

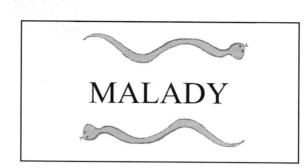 MALADY

 MALICIOUS

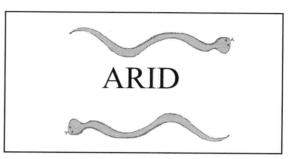 ARID

 SABOTAGE

 DECLINE

 CHASTISE

 PERISH

 HAPLESS

 CEASE

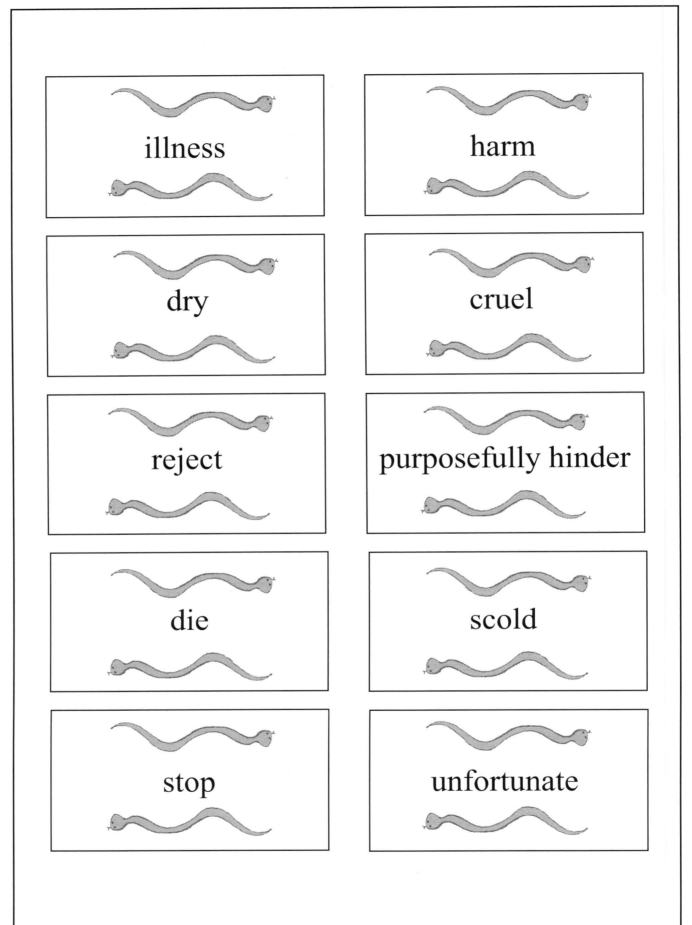

illness

harm

dry

cruel

reject

purposefully hinder

die

scold

stop

unfortunate

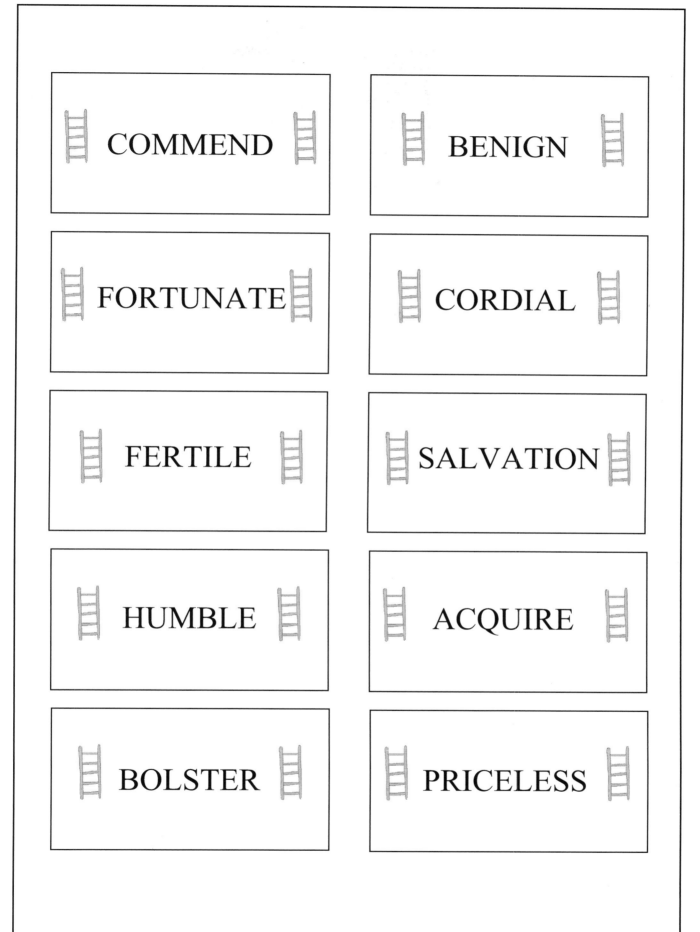

COMMEND

BENIGN

FORTUNATE

CORDIAL

FERTILE

SALVATION

HUMBLE

ACQUIRE

BOLSTER

PRICELESS

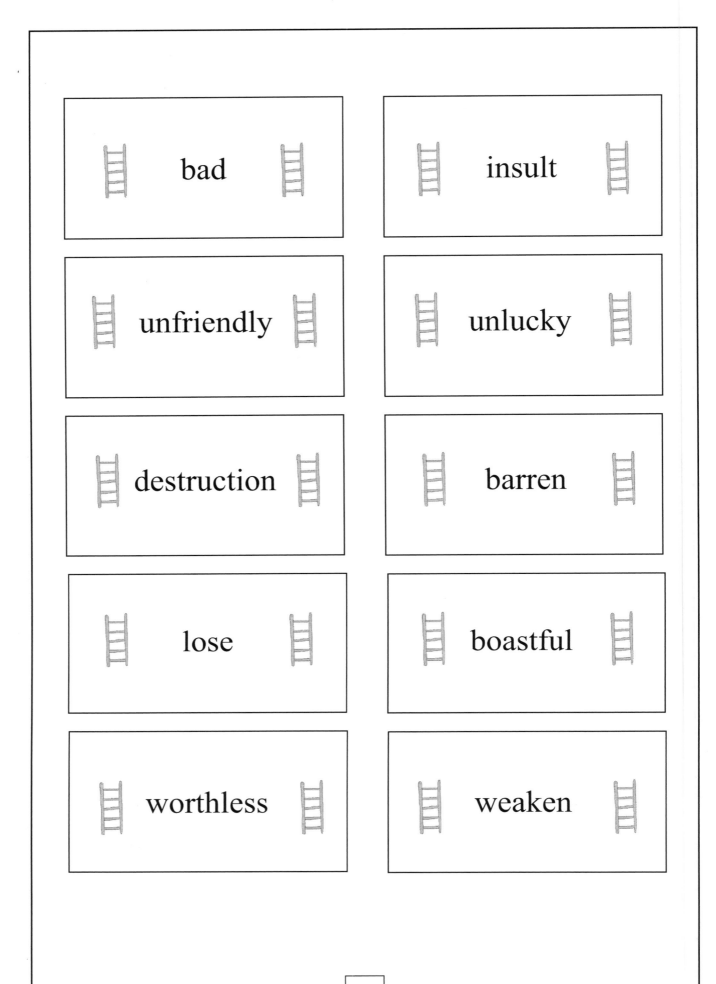

bad

insult

unfriendly

unlucky

destruction

barren

lose

boastful

worthless

weaken

Snakes and Ladders Board

100	99	98	97	96	95	94	93	92	91
81	82	83	84	85	86	87	88	89	90
80	79	78	77	76	75	74	73	72	71
61	62	63	64	65	66	67	68	69	70
60	59	58	57	56	55	54	53	52	51
41	42	43	44	45	46	47	48	49	50
40	39	38	37	36	35	34	33	32	31
21	22	23	24	25	26	27	28	29	30
20	19	18	17	16	15	14	13	12	11
1	2	3	4	5	6	7	8	9	10

FUNNY FACES

Pictures can be useful in helping to remember vocabulary and also stimulate discussion about synonyms.

In these examples:

Appropriate answers could range from -

- Happy   - Excited
- Overjoyed   - Thrilled
- Delighted   - Pleased
- Radiant   - Buoyant

- Silly   - Crazy
- Childish   - Ridiculous
- Inappropriate   - Preposterous
- Nonsensical   - Ludicrous

Cut out the cards on the following pages and try to identify the emotion or idea being expressed. Possible answers will be on the back of each card.

What other synonyms can match these words? See if you can think of at least two adjectives to describe the funny face!

patriot loyalist, nationalist	**irate** mad, upset, angry
jovial affable, festive	**affluent** rich, wealthy
bilingual	**feeble** weak
exasperated agitated, annoyed	**nimble** agile, quick
despondent dejected, depressed	**valiant** gallant, courageous

affable amiable, cheerful	**bashful** shy, self-conscious
vain conceited, arrogant	**haughty** snobbish, snooty
malicious hateful, vicious	**industrious** hard-working
perplexed bewildered, puzzled	**indolent** lazy, lethargic
deceitful deceptive, misleading	**prodigy** gifted, genius

Practice Page

WORD ATTACK

This is a two-player game. The objective of the game is to sink the other player's ships, before they can sink yours! Spend some time learning the word meanings for two of the word sets (opposite) before beginning the game. For example, use sets A and B in the first week.

Setup: Each player receives a game board page. Cut out the 5 game pieces and lay them on the MY SHIPS grid (Alternately, draw in the ships on your paper). The ships must be placed either horizontally or vertically, as shown in the picture. Do not allow your opponent to see where you have placed your ships!

Each player should also get a list of words.

Gameplay: Players take turns making guesses as to where their opponent's ships might be, using grid coordinates. Guesses should be recorded in the MY GUESSES grid so that players have a complete record and don't guess the same space twice.

Before taking a turn, a player must give a correct definition or synonym to one of the words from their opponent's word list. If they answer incorrectly, then they miss the chance to guess a coordinate.

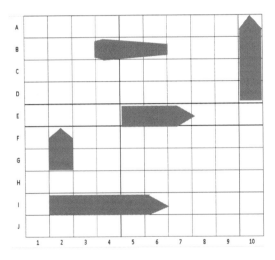

In the above example, the submarine is covering coordinates B4, B5, B6

Once all of the words on a list have been used, start again with the same list. This will help reinforce comprehension.

When a player guesses a grid space, for example D-10, the other player must say either "HIT" or "MISS," depending on whether their ship is placed in that grid. In the example above, it would be a "HIT." When all spaces the ship is covering have been guessed by the opponent, the player should announce that their ship has been sunk by saying, "You sunk my ship!"

The game ends when one of the players has lost all of their ships.

Note: This game can be played many times using the different sets of battle words.

ATTACK WORDS

SET A

INDUSTRIOUS
DEMOLISH
ORCA
GOWN
OASIS
AWNING
CONTEMPORARY
COMPASS
ABUNDANCE
PALINDROME

SET B

TEPEE
ESCALATED
LIVID
SEVERE
HABERDASHERY
URN
MINISTER
CONDEMN
CONDIMENT
EXPENDITURE

SET C

STRUT
MAIZE
TORSO
FLAWLESS
IMPEDE
FORGO
ABHORRENT
VERTEBRATE
YOLK
MAIM

SET D

GRUESOME
BURDEN
FUTILE
UMPIRE
FATHOM
COARSE
MIRTH
LIABLE
GAVEL
NAUSEOUS

ATTACK WORDS

SET E

INFLUENCE
FERMENT
VILLAIN
JEER
DILUTED
AMPHIBIAN
POST
PLACID
DEARTH
FABRICATION

SET F

OPTIMISTIC
DIRE
SOVEREIGN
CROCHET
AVIARY
AID
CHAPERONE
FALTER
OPAQUE
APPALLED

SET G

TEMPLATE
AUBERGINE
GAUNTLET
VERANDAH
NOVICE
DISSIPATE
NONENTITY
CLARIFY
PRECIPITATION
REBUKE

SET H

POSTPONED
PUNGENT
BESIEGED
TABLET
ATRIUM
THEATRE
AMASS
GARGANTUAN
BLACKLIST
PULSATE

Word Attack Game Pieces

Player 1

Agile Aircraft Carrier (5 spaces)

Lethal Large ship (4 spaces)

Deceptive Destroyer (3 spaces)

Swift Submarine (3 spaces)

Perilous Patrol Boat (2 spaces)

Player 2

Agile Aircraft Carrier (5 spaces)

Lethal Large ship (4 spaces)

Deceptive Destroyer (3 spaces)

Swift Submarine (3 spaces)

Perilous Patrol Boat (2 spaces)

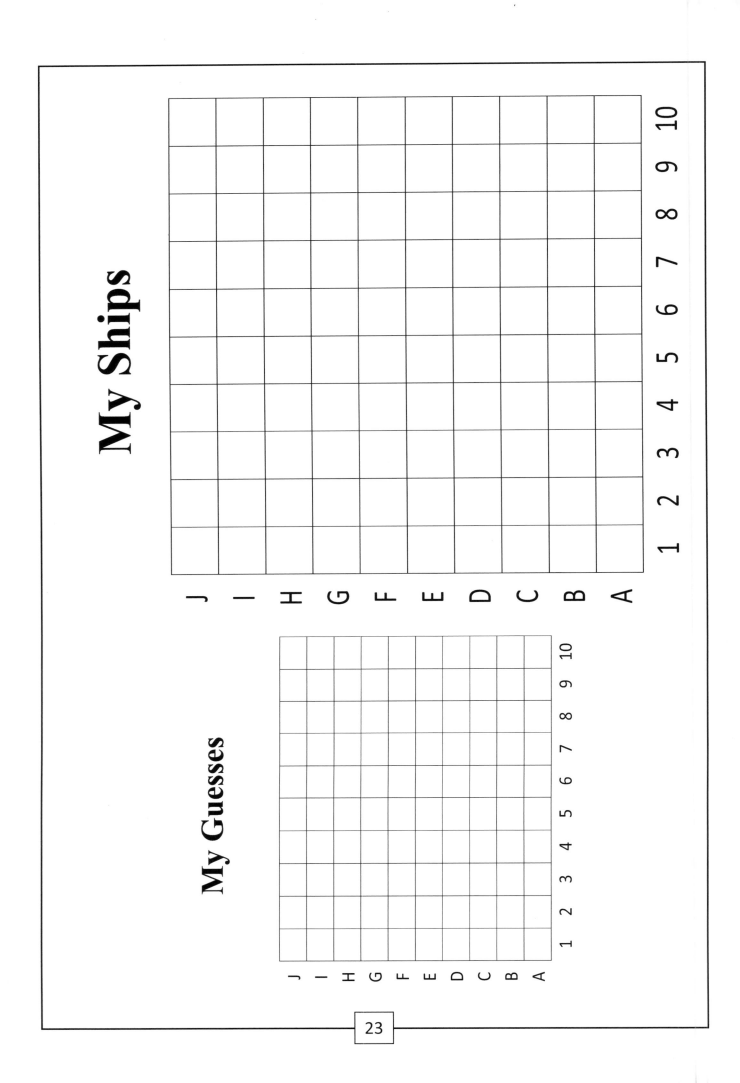

My Ships

My Guesses

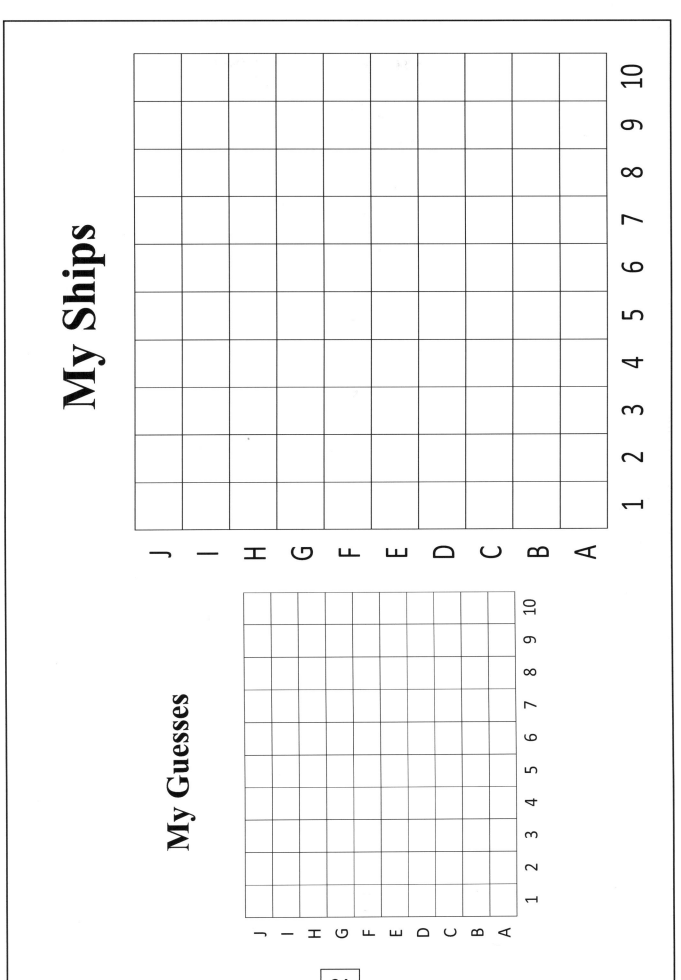

My Ships

My Guesses

SPREADING THE WORD

This is a technique that helps to reinforce words by giving a clue, and then challenging you to find the answer hidden between two different words.

This type of question is featured on some Eleven Plus exams. However, now you can improve your vocabulary whilst finding the words.

Examples:

A healthy drink   car<u>ton</u> <u>ic</u>on = tonic

Material used for surfacing roads   gui<u>tar</u> <u>mac</u>aroni = tarmac

Severe physical or mental suffering   distribu<u>tor</u> <u>ment</u>al = torment

Clue: Find:

1. lively   wasp   rye
2. a living place   plod   gentle
3. get rid of   you   street
4. work hard   into   illegal
5. not very often   counsel   dome
6. get bigger   reflex   panda
7. someone that dies for a cause   grammar   tyre
8. the very top   sum   mitten
9. joker   cow   itinerary
10. left alone, not planted   downfall   owl

SPREADING THE WORD

11. neither warm nor cold	step	idea
12. bring into a country	shrimp	orthodontist
13. a promise	boa	three
14. arm or leg	slim	breach
15. to set light to	kind	lent
16. fake, not genuine	rash	amiable
17. big, enormous	lava	stream
18. to put completely into water	simmer	send
19. a loud noise	bend	include
20. a disease or illness	grandma	lady
21. clever	last	utensil
22. make a pained face	pilgrim	acetone
23. successor, next in line	tithe	irregular
24. something given	hairdo	national
25. a group of notes sounded together	anchor	destiny
26. chemical element, fluorescent lighting	insane	onward
27. not active	eyelid	lethargic
28. of good behaviour and principle	tremor	almost
29. keeps a boat from moving	man	choral
30. give someone the story	abide	briefly
31. staunch, unyielding	homestead	fastidious
32. not gregarious	mimic	oyster

FORTUNE TELLER

This is a game you might have played in school before, but now it can be used to help learn new words. First, find the definition of each word. Use the glossary to make sure you are learning the correct definitions before you practise.

Cut and fold the opposite page as you would for a fortune teller game:

- Lay the paper with the printed side facing down on the table and fold the four corners into the centre
- Flip over and fold the four corners along the lines into the centre
- Fold over and back (one at a time) on the diagonal, vertical and horizontal lines to make the fortune teller flexible
- Place fingers underneath the flaps to hold the completed model (as shown below)

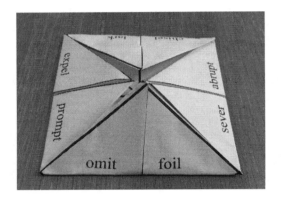

Step One – folded corners

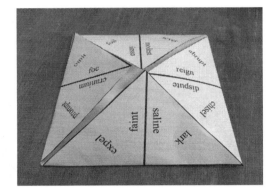

Step Two – folded corners

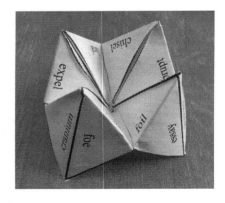

Completed model after folding along lines and fingers placed

FORTUNE TELLER

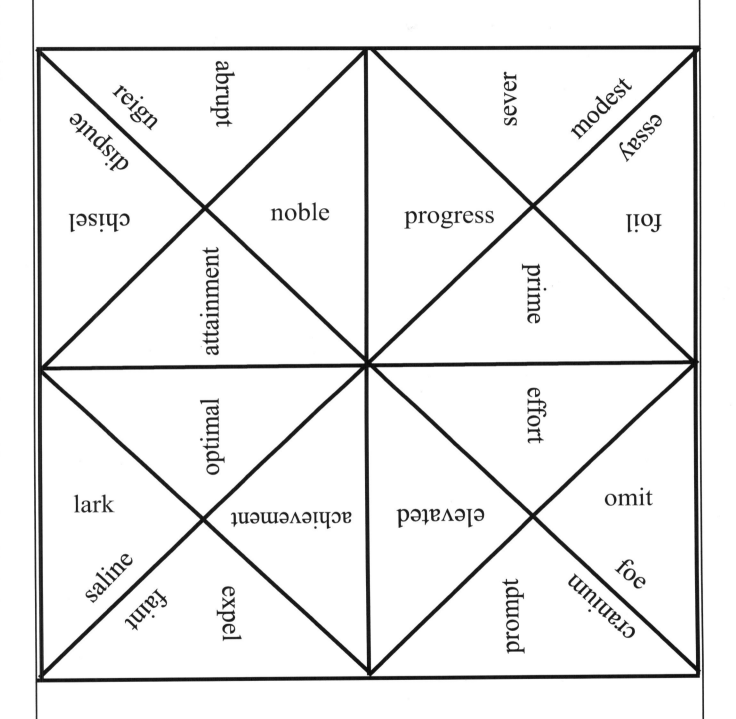

FORTUNE TELLER

This page left intentionally blank

FORTUNE TELLER

How to Play: This game is intended as a tactile way to practise words. Play in the traditional manner, however you may only move fingers if you can give a definition of your chosen word.

Start with the fortune teller closed and pick one of the words showing on the outside. Move fingers in and out the number of times that matches the number of letters in the word. Use the words on the inside until you have completed three turns correctly, and then you may open one of the inside flaps to find a new word (or fortune).

CROSSWORD

Use the word bank at the bottom of the page to help you complete the puzzle.

ACROSS

1. To improve
4. The basement
6. Last but one
9. A measure, quantity or frequency
10. Give way!
11. A bag
13. Small house or meeting place
15. To plant, or a female pig
16. Speaks Arabic, German and Mandarin
17. Wonder, Amazement
19. The enemy is this
21. Ireland
22. To leave out
23. Where a wild animal lives (rhymes with bear)
24. A tough situation

DOWN

2. Not me – a female sheep
3. A weather man/woman
4. Cantankerous
5. Dishonest or unprincipled
6. To die
7. See the sign
8. Holds an artist's work
12. Skill, especially with hands
14. Respect and admiration
18. Great energy or enthusiasm
19. Successor
20. Part of the ear

WORD BANK

ADVERSITY	LOBE	ZEAL	YIELD
ROGUE	OMIT	LODGE	AWE
CELLAR	CRANKY	ESTEEM	LINGUIST
METEOROLOGIST	EWE	HOSTILE	SOW
PENULTIMATE	LAIR	PERISH	NOTICE
DEXTERITY	HEIR	RATE	SACK
EASEL	EIRE	REFORM	

CROSSWORD

SHOP 'TIL YOU DROP

Marilu's grandfather has given her a shopping list. Her problem is, she doesn't know where to buy the various items. Show her where to go to find each item. Write the item underneath the appropriate shop on the next page.

Can you think of any other items that might be available at these shops?

SHOPPING LIST

SHAWL

SIDEBOARD

PLAICE

PENDANT

CULOTTES

UPHOLSTERED WING BACK

PEONY

BROOCH

REMNANTS

BUREAU

FUTON

GOWN

RAIMENT

ENCYCLOPEDIA

ARMOIRE

RHODODDENDRON

PLIERS

BERET

CUFF LINKS

TEXTILES

TARTAN

ANTHOLOGY

LOCKET

CRAVAT

HADDOCK

Jazz's Jewellery

Fishmonger

Freda's Furniture

Fred's Fashions

Flo the Florist

Book Store

Sew 'n' Sew

THE HEAT IS ON!

The weather station forecasts that the temperature will rise! Cut out the words on the opposite page and discuss where they should go on the thermometer:

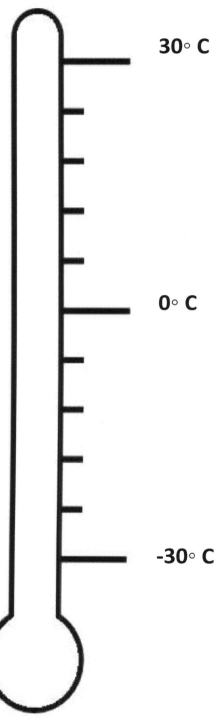

30° C

0° C

-30° C

biting	nippy	tropical
temperate	inclement	baking
balmy	sweltering	searing
tepid	chilly	frigid
lukewarm	scorching	icy
sultry	raw	freezing
sizzling	clement	close

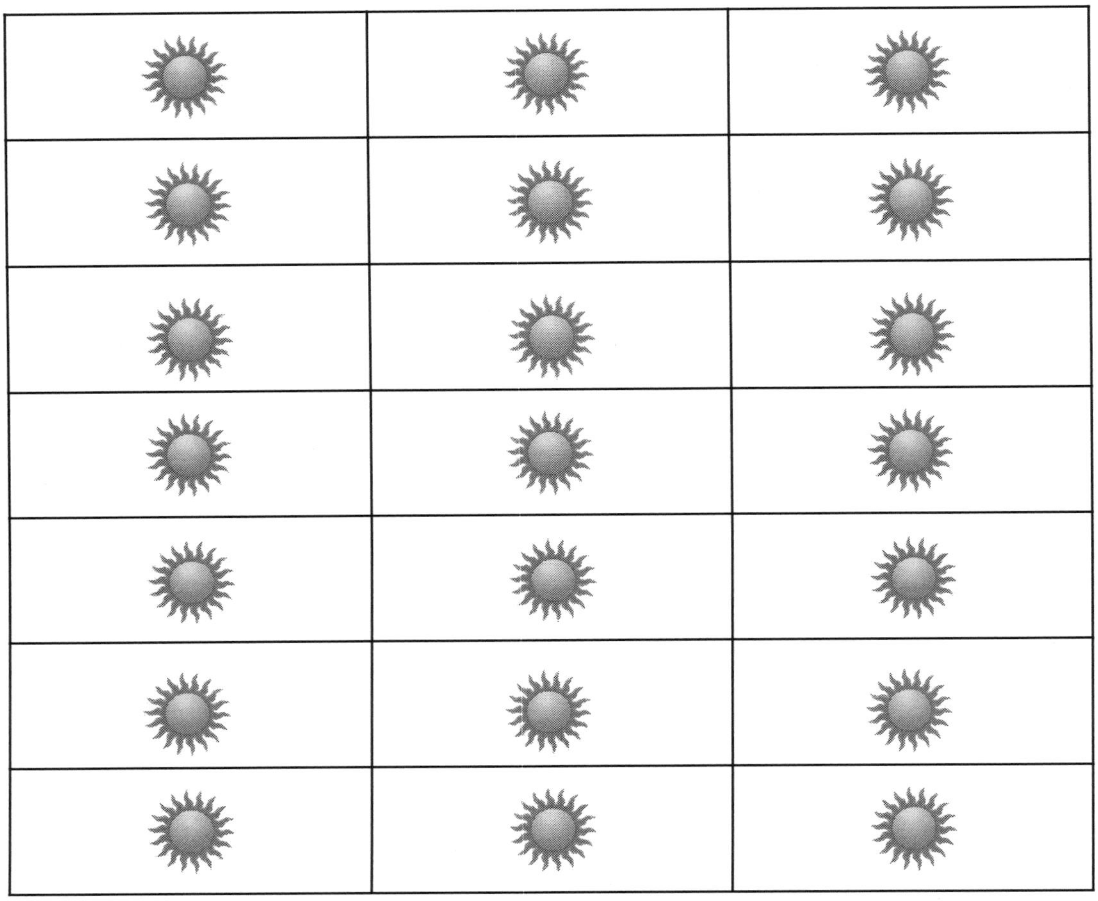

COLLECTING CLUES

Find the collective term. Some of these are tricky, do not be afraid to use the Answer Key. The first example has been given.

CLUE	COLLECTIVE		NOUNS
Ground Defenders	**army**	of	ants
Fill your suitcase	_____	of	wolves
A great feeling	_____	of	lions
Peas live here	_____	of	whales
Put it in the bin	_____	of	puppies
Causing trouble	_____	of	mice
To kill someone	_____	of	crows
Hide and surprise	_____	of	tigers
Bird's home	_____	of	vipers
Blushing with it	_____	of	riches
TV programme leader	_____	of	angels
Grey rock used for roof tiles	_____	of	candidates
String, wind, brass and percussion form this	_____	of	crickets
An explosive collection	_____	of	guns
Beer is often carried in this	_____	of	laughs
Shake a little	_____	of	arrows
Somewhere to sleep	_____	of	oysters
Government's home	_____	of	owls
Swim here	_____	of	typists
Reef, double and slip are these	_____	of	toads
First finger	_____	of	names
Grab hold!	_____	of	eggs

HOMOPHONE PAIRS
HOMOPHONE PAIRS

A homophone is a word that is pronounced the same as another word, but has a different meaning.

The cards on the following pages make sets of homophone pairs. After cutting out the cards, spread them out over your table. Take it in turns to lift two cards. If they ARE homophone pairs AND you can define both meanings, you keep the pair. If they are not homophone pairs, return them to the table and the next player has a turn.

The winner collects the most pairs.

Do not feel that you need to use all of the cards in every game. Twenty new words to learn in a week is plenty. If you do not know the meanings, look in the glossary at the back of the book.

Example:

Loot = money and valuables, often illegally seized

Lute = a pear-shaped, string instrument

pairs	pears
leak	leek
rays	raise
lax	lacks
hoarse	horse
axes	axis
guise	guys
base	bass
foul	fowl
based	baste

homophone pairs	homophone pairs
homophone pairs	homophone pairs
homophone pairs	homophone pairs
homophone pairs	homophone pairs
homophone pairs	homophone pairs
homophone pairs	homophone pairs
homophone pairs	homophone pairs
homophone pairs	homophone pairs
homophone pairs	homophone pairs
homophone pairs	homophone pairs

dense	dents
chord	cord
cent	scent
callous	callus
boar	bore
bald	bawled
ewes	yews
genes	jeans
real	reel
need	knead

homophone pairs	homophone pairs
homophone pairs	homophone pairs
homophone pairs	homophone pairs
homophone pairs	homophone pairs
homophone pairs	homophone pairs
homophone pairs	homophone pairs
homophone pairs	homophone pairs
homophone pairs	homophone pairs
homophone pairs	homophone pairs
homophone pairs	homophone pairs

morning	mourning
gait	gate
beach	beech
shoot	chute
principle	principal
waive	wave
yoke	yolk
symbol	cymbal
rye	wry
role	roll

homophone pairs	homophone pairs
homophone pairs	homophone pairs
homophone pairs	homophone pairs
homophone pairs	homophone pairs
homophone pairs	homophone pairs
homophone pairs	homophone pairs
homophone pairs	homophone pairs
homophone pairs	homophone pairs
homophone pairs	homophone pairs
homophone pairs	homophone pairs

Tongue Twisters

Try and memorise these tongue twisters and say them as fast as you can!

1. VAIN VIOLET THOUGHT VISCOSE VESTS VERY SWISH.

2. SQUEAMISH SQUIRRELS SQUEAL AND SQUABBLE.

3. NOAH NEVER KNEW A NEATER NOVEL.

4. CUNNING KATIE CAUGHT CLIVE CLIMBING.

5. PETER PESTERED PIPPA TO PICK A PROPER PACKET.

6. ON MOST MONDAYS, MAX, MOLLY AND MANDY MINGLE.

7. RELIABLE REILLY RECTIFIED ROBBY'S ROTTEN WRITING.

8. IDA IRRITATED IRATE IRIS INCESSANTLY.

9. LARRY LIES LUCIDLY.

10. HOARDING HILDA HID HER HULA HOOP IN HAMPSHIRE

11. PERFECT PETER PERPETUATES PROFESSIONAL PUNS.

12. TARDY TURTLES TRAIN IN TRANQUILTY.

Can you work out what they mean?

SENTENCE CHARADES

This is a game for two or more players.

Be sure you know the meanings of the following words::

IGNITED = lit

GINGERLY = carefully

FURIOUS = angry

CHERISHED = cared for

GEM = jewel

EXQUISITE = extremely beautiful

ASCENDED = went up

CAPTIVE = prisoner

MEANDERS = bends

UNPALATABLE = bad tasting

TALONS = large claws (bird)

SERENADE = sing romantically

PHOBIA = fear

CRANIUM = brain

INFLEXIBLE = rigid

Players will have ONE MINUTE to look at all of the cards. Cards should then be cut out and placed face-down in a pile.

Players take turns to lift a card from the pile, and then act out a sentence. Other players attempt to guess the sentence..

Charade Sentence Cards

I ignited the fire gingerly but there was a furious blaze.	I cherished the glistening gem as it was exquisite.
The judge was inflexible and wouldn't free the captive.	The dog ascended the stairs
The river meanders for many miles.	The cook found the cake unpalatable.
The boyfriend serenaded his girlfriend just for fun.	Eagles have enormous talons.
The cat had a phobia regarding spiders.	My cranium hurts!

CHARADES	CHARADES
CHARADES	CHARADES
CHARADES	CHARADES
CHARADES	CHARADES
CHARADES	CHARADES

Rock, Paper, Scissors

As a fun break, play the old stand-by game of "Rock, Paper, Scissors" with a twist – use these sets of new words:

	Game A	**Game B**	**Game C**
ROCK	flint	granite	quartz
PAPER	parchment	papyrus	leaf
SCISSORS	scythe	guillotine	cleaver

The Rules (in case you forgot):

Rock crushes
Scissors

Scissors cut Paper

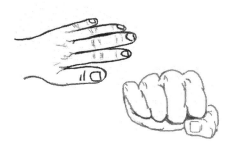

Paper covers Rock

DOT · TO · DOT

Do this dot to dot using the clues given for in order. Use the letters in the answer to connect the dots and complete the picture. The first answer has been given.

Clues:	**Answer**
not transparent	opaque
desire	_____
neutral	_____
moan	_____
worried	_____
exaggerate	_____
careful with money	_____
outside edge	_____
untidy	_____
magical	_____
a steady beat	_____
to go into	_____
difficult to carry	_____
changeable personality	_____
stick out	_____
rude	_____
beginner	_____
not urban	_____
get faster	_____

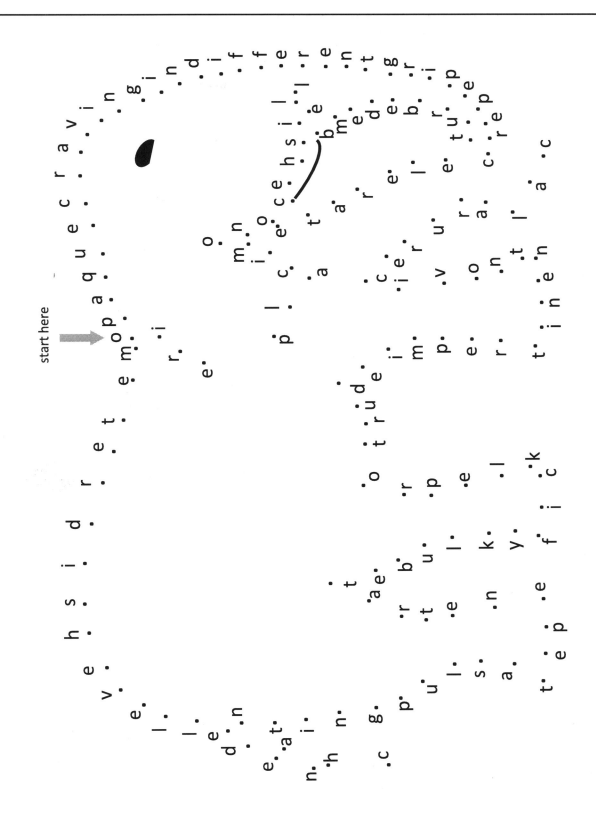

start here

BONUS QUESTION:
WHAT KIND OF CREATURE AM I?

ANSWER: _ _ C _ Y _ ER _

Dial a Clue

Use the clue and the number to work out the mystery words. You can look at these examples to see if there is a pattern:

CLUE	CODE	MYSTERY WORD
ONLY	6 3 7 3	MERE
CENTRE	4 8 2	HUB

"May I have a clue, please."

53

Dial a Clue

CLUE	CODE	MYSTERY WORD
DONATE	4 4 8 3	_____
DEBATE	8 2 5 5	_____
INTERVAL	2 7 3 2 5	_____
AJAR	6 7 3 6	_____
SCRUFFY	7 4 2 2 2 9	_____
CONTEMPORARY	6 6 3 3 7 6	_____
DELAYED	5 2 8 3	_____
SKETCH	3 7 2 9	_____
FRET	9 6 7 7 9	_____
LABYRINTH	6 2 9 4	_____
AGILE	6 4 6 2 5 3	_____
AVOID	7 4 8 6	_____
FOUNDATION	2 2 7 3	_____
SUBSEQUENT	6 3 9 8	_____
CRUEL	8 6 5 4 6 3	_____
COMBINE	2 5 3 6 3	_____
DOZEN	8 9 3 5 8 3	_____

SCATTER PLATTER

YOU HAVE 20 CARDS. ON THE MAIN SIDE THERE IS A **WORD**. ON THE BACK OF EACH CARD ARE ONE SYNONYM AND ONE ANTONYM THAT MATCH THE MAIN WORD.

Cut out or photocopy the cards.

After practising the words, place them with the main word facing up on the table. Look at them altogether for a few minutes.

The first player should then remove three of the cards. The other player(s) then must guess which cards have been removed.

Players can score one point for guessing correctly the missing word, one point for the synonym, and one point for the antonym.

It is not necessary to use all the cards in every game.

constant	passive
wholesome	absurd
restrict	torment
squander	sugar-coat
string	baffle

accepting active	non-stop temporary
ridiculous sensible	healthy impure
bother comfort	limit loosen
disguise agitate	waste save
confound enlighten	cord individual

bend	common
coarse	notice
accept	swollen
weak	private

familiar rare	warp straighten
regard ignore	rough smooth
bloated deflated	agree reject
confidential public	frail robust

Draw the Scene

Use your artistic skills to draw a scene, featuring all of the elements as requested, in any order.

Example: A **dinghy** on a **tempestuous** sea

A **dinghy** is a small boat
Tempestuous means strong and turbulent

1.   Witches cackling by a craggy cliff

2.   A pedestrian wearing a poncho

3.   A treacherous ascent

Draw the Scene

4. A dilapidated fort

5. An absurdly wealthy lady

6. A highway intersection

Draw the Scene

7. A scene set at twilight

8. A concealed entrance slightly ajar

9. A picnic hamper with lemon cordial

ODD **ONE** OUT

Find the word that doesn't belong in the following sentences.

Example

HOAX   SHAM      FORGERY   COPY

1. CLARIFY   HAZY   HIDDEN   OBSCURE   VAGUE

2. BERET   TRAINER   BROGUE   STILETTO   SANDAL

3. POINTLESS   USELESS   WEAK   INEPT   CAPABLE

4. WOOL   NYLON   COTTON   SILK   HEMP

5. STILL   ERRATIC   CALM   STABLE   CONSTANT

6. MOTIVATED   IDLE   PURPOSEFUL   ACTIVE   KEEN

7. MIMIC   REPEAT   ORIGINATE   COPY   RE-DO

8. POSITIVE   AUSPICIOUS   OMINOUS   ENCOURAGING   PROMISING

9. HUB   PERIPHERY   CENTRE   INNERMOST   MIDDLE

10. SUPPORT   DISCOURAGE   PROMOTE   BOLSTER   ADVOCATE

ODD **ONE** OUT

Find the word that doesn't belong in the following sentences.

11. ELDERLY   INFANTILE   YOUNG   JUNIOR   IMMATURE

12. SAW   HAMMER   CHISEL   SCREW DRIVER   NAIL

13. LIMB   HEART   LIVER   KIDNEY   STOMACH

14. INCISION   CLOSE   KNIT   HEAL   STITCH   PATCH

15. CROCODILE   ALLIGATOR   TURTLE   LIZARD   SALAMANDER

16. DEMOLISH DECIMATE RUIN ANNIHILATE RENOVATE PULVERISE

17. EYE   MICROSCOPE   CAMERA   TELEVISION   CONTACT

18. HAMMER   DISCUS   ARROW   DISCUSS   SHOT PUT

19. CRAVAT   BOWLER   BONNET   TRILBY   BOATER

20. DWELLING   SHELTER   TEAK   TENT   TEPEE

21. MAIZE   TOMATO   POTATO   AUBERGINE   BAGUETTE

22. SECONDARY   SUBSIDIARY   JUNIOR   CHIEF   ASSISTANT

Synonym Shake

Cut out the cards and shape, which forms a 10-sided die, decahedron (or decagon). Fold and stick (or tape) the flaps to make the shape as shown below.

Draw one of the five cards (globe, grab, curve, crowd, question) then toss the decahedron. Use the glossary to check.

If the word facing up on the decahedron has the same meaning as the word on the card, you score a point.

First player to ten points wins.

	Player 1	Player 2
Game 1		
Game 2		
Game 3		
Game 4		

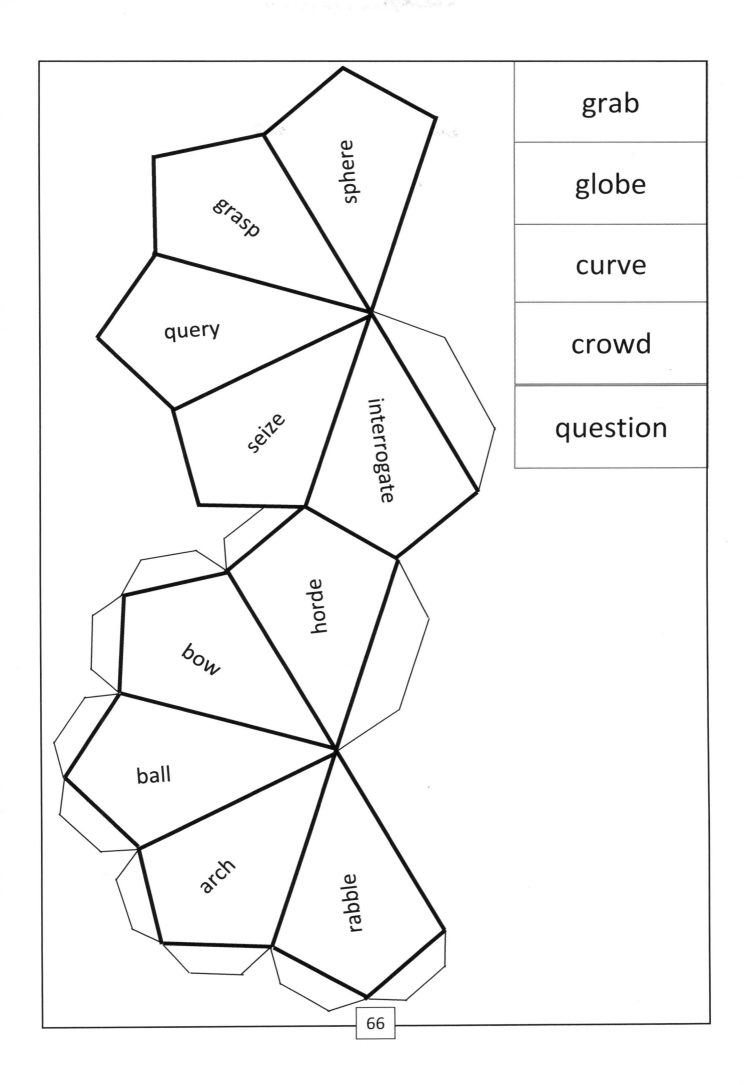

grab

globe

curve

crowd

question

sphere

grasp

query

seize

interrogate

horde

bow

ball

arch

rabble

This page left intentionally blank

Hang On Man!

We take a departure from the old standard game of Hangman to Hang On, Man! Spend some time discovering the meanings of the words on the next page before you play.

The player drawing first starts by choosing a word. On a piece of paper, draw spaces for each of the letters in the word. The other player has to guess a letter. If the guess is correct, then write the letter in the appropriate space(s). If the player misses a letter, draw one part of the Hang On Man. Keep going until the player can guess the word and give its meaning.

If the player misses 7 tries, then the stick figure is completed and they lose that round. You can also use more words from the glossary.

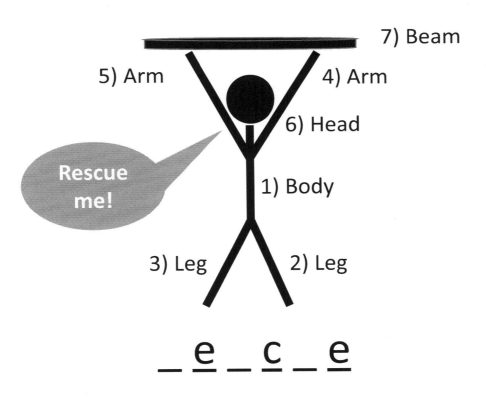

_ e _ c _ e

Hang On Man!

LIST A	LIST B
taboo	discus
exhale	estuary
deceit	petroleum
exploit	relate
serenity	indispensable
financial	martyr
flippant	affable
imply	subdued
despot	orthodontist
voluntary	convent
nullify	lithe
coarse	glutton
ewe	enigma
grieve	trawler
slovenly	cassette
extract	suede
cajole	sermon
static	equator
persevere	pique

Hang On Man!

SOARING SYNONYMS

Find a synonym for the given word. Using the point scoring values for each letter below, try to find the highest scoring synonym for each of the words. A score lower than the number given is worth zero, whilst any scores higher than the number will count as double.

A	B	C	D	E	F	G	H		I	J	K	L	M	N	O	P		Q	R	S	T	U	V	W	X	Y	Z
1	3	3	4	1	4	2	3		1	5	4	3	3	4	1	4		5	3	2	2	1	5	3	5	2	5

EXAMPLE

LAVISH   15

ANSWER

EXTRAVAGANT (27 points) = 48 ⬅ **Best Answer**
1 5 23 15 12 1 42

LUSH (9 points) = **zero** (less than 15 points)
3 12 3

EXCESSIVE (21 points) = 42
1 5 31 22151

OPULENT (15 points) = 15 (no bonus)
14 12 14 2

As you can see, some words can have many different answers. The goal is to try and come up with as many different words as possible.

SOARING SYNONYMS

A B C D E F G H   I J K L M N O P   Q R S T U V W X Y Z
1 3 3 4 1 4 2 3   1 5 4 3 3 4 1 4   5 3 2 2 1 5 3 5 2 5

	Number Given
MIMIC	10
CREATE	9
FAMISHED	15
COMPLETE	10
COMPLICATE	11
RENOWNED	12
DISOBEY	11
RELEASE	9
ATTEMPT	7
ARID	8
DEFECT	11
OBTAIN	5
WEARY	11
ARTIFICIAL	10
SCEPTICAL	19
DESPONDENT	9
IMPOVERISHED	9
THREATENED	13
OMINOUS	9

SYNONYM MAZE

This is a maze of synonyms. From the start position words can go forwards, backwards, up or down, but each word is always in a straight line, but not overlapping. Can you follow the journey from *Start* so that **each new word is a synonym of the previous word**, until you reach *Finish*?

The first two steps have been completed for you.

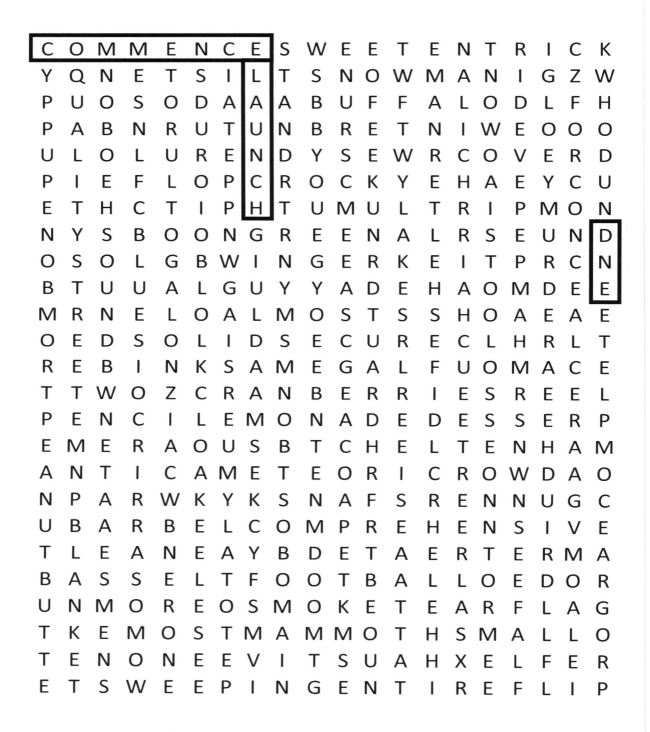

```
C O M M E N C E S W E E T E N T R I C K
Y Q N E T S I L T S N O W M A N I G Z W
P U O S O D A A A B U F F A L O D L F H
P A B N R U T U N B R E T N I W E O O O
U L O L U R E N D Y S E W R C O V E R D
P I E F L O P C R O C K Y E H A E Y C U
E T H C T I P H T U M U L T R I P M O N
N Y S B O O N G R E E N A L R S E U N D
O S O L G B W I N G E R K E I T P R C N
B T U U A L G U Y Y A D E H A O M D E E
M R N E L O A L M O S T S S H O A E A E
O E D S O L I D S E C U R E C L H R L T
R E B I N K S A M E G A L F U O M A C E
T T W O Z C R A N B E R R I E S R E E L
P E N C I L E M O N A D E D E S S E R P
E M E R A O U S B T C H E L T E N H A M
A N T I C A M E T E O R I C R O W D A O
N P A R W K Y K S N A F S R E N N U G C
U B A R B E L C O M P R E H E N S I V E
T L E A N E A Y B D E T A E R T E R M A
B A S S E L T F O O T B A L L O E D O R
U N M O R E O S M O K E T E A R F L A G
T K E M O S T M A M M O T H S M A L L O
T E N O N E E V I T S U A H X E L F E R
E T S W E E P I N G E N T I R E F L I P
```

FIVE POINTS

In this game, use the clues to prompt the player to guess the key word. There are five clues that should lead to the correct answer.

Start with clue 5, if the player guesses on that clue they receive 10 points. If a player guesses on clue 4, they receive 4 points; clue 3 = 3 points; clue 2 = 2 points; clue 1 = 1 point.

EDGE	**PUZZLE**	**DREAM**
1. Fence	1. Riddle	1. Imagine
2. Ring	2. Confuse	2. Fantasy
3. Boundary	3. Baffle	3. Thought
4. Enclosure	4. Perplex	4. Delusion
5. Perimeter	5. Conundrum	5. Trance
HOME	**EXCITING**	**FIND**
1. House	1. Wild	1. Discover
2. Lodging	2. Dramatic	2. Treasure Trove
3. Dwelling	3. Thrilling	3. Unearth
4. Residence	4. Exhilarating	4. Detect
5. Sanctuary	5. Stimulating	5. Acquisition

FIVE POINTS

EXPENSIVE

1. Overpriced
2. Costly
3. Extravagant
4. Excessive
5. Exorbitant

LUCKY

1. Favourable
2. Fortunate
3. Charmed
4. Fortuitous
5. Auspicious

CLEVER

1. Intelligent
2. Brilliant
3. Gifted
4. Cunning
5. Adroit

SHARP

1. Pointy
2. Prickly
3. Jagged
4. Acute
5. Whetted

WATER

1. Rain
2. Liquid
3. Sleet
4. Moisture
5. Precipitation

HUNGRY

1. Starving
2. Unsatisfied
3. Craving
4. Famished
5. Ravenous

Colour Me Slowly

Colour the picture with colours that match the words. Try to use exact colours to decorate the snail. If you don't have a full set of colours, use the best fit for the major colour group – Red, Green, Orange, Grey, Blue, Yellow, Brown and Purple.

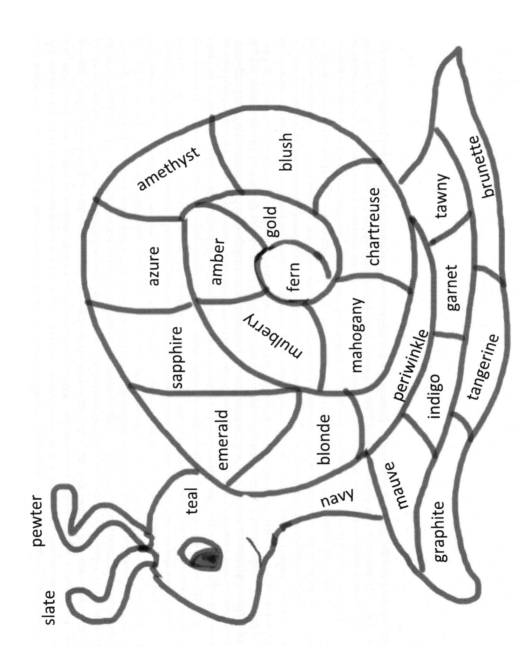

Ridiculous Rhymes

Read the ridiculous rhymes below. Let these rhymes help you remember the definitions of the key words given.

Key Words
Emulsion, Arrogant, Morose, Conceal, Admire, Distinct, Volatile, Esteem, Hesitate, Embark, Allocate, Fatal, Flaw, Incognito, Lexicon, Constrict, Hapless, Poise, Prohibit

1. The kitchen painted in purple emulsion
   Made Katie sick with utter revulsion

2. Tina was such an arrog-ant
   She boasted to the eleph-ant

3. The morose gent could not conceal
   The romantic heart ache he did feel

4. The horses they did all admire
   The unicorn singing in the choir

5. Rahid's look was quite distinct
   Perhaps it was the way he winked

6. The volcano's mood was so volatile
   The villagers ran for half a mile

7. The player was held in great esteem
   When he scored a hat trick for the team

Ridiculous Rhymes

8. Hedgy Hedgehog wasn't one to hesitate
   Her greatest fear was being too late

9. On a perilous journey did Sam embark
   But lost his footing in the dark

10. Ted was having difficulty trying to allocate
    Sufficient time to write a report on Alexander The Great

11. Mildred's plan had a fatal flaw
    Space travel with zebras was against international law

12. Amongst the thousands of revellers, did no one know
    The man in the hat and sunglasses was incognito

13. Eleven Plus vocabulary she had done.
    She began to feel like a lexicon

14. The snake liked to tighten and constrict
    The hapless victim she had picked

15. The ballerina had such perfect poise,
    She pirouetted above the noise

16. I'm certain that we must prohibit
    Gorillas singing at the exhibit

Find the vertical word linking all of the other words

1).

```
        S  C  H  O  L  A  R
                 E  D  U  C  A  T  E
           T  E  A  C  H  E  R
           T  U  T  O  R
  P  E  D  A  G  O  G  U  E
           I  N  S  T  R  U  C  T  O  R
           M  A  S  T  E  R
  T  R  A  I  N  E  R
```

2)

```
                          C  A  N  N  Y
                          C  A  R  E
                       P  R  U  D  E  N  C  E
                 A  T  T  E  N  T  I  O  N
        D  E  L  I  B  E  R  A  T  I  O  N
                          T  H  O  U  G  H  T
           V  I  G  I  L  E  N  C  E
```

3)

```
        D  I  S  F  I  G  U  R  E
        I  M  P  A  I  R
  D  E  S  T  R  O  Y
  D  E  M  O  L  I  S  H
  D  E  F  I  L  E
```

4)

```
        C H A N G E
        M O D I F Y
          T A I L O R
      S H A P E
      A L T E R
```

5)

```
      S P R E A D
    S T R E T C H
        L A T I T U D E
        C A P A C I T Y
        H O R I Z O N
```

6)

```
              A
              I N C O G N I T O
    P S E U D O
              U N I D E N T I F I E D
              M Y S T E R I O U S
      U N N A M E D
              J O H N D O E
              U N C R E D I T E D
              S E C R E T
```

BONUS – Match the word below that goes best with each set:

INTRIGUE   UNIVERSITY   SCAR   DISTANCE
MORPH   CONSIDERATION

Using the photos, match the flowers with their names.

DELPHINIUM   CARNATION   HYDRANGEA

PEONY   CHRYSANTHEMUM   GLADIOLUS

BABY'S BREATH   SNAPDRAGON   AZALEA

CROCUS   DAHLIA   FREESIA

GERANIUM   HIBISCUS   JASMINE

LILAC   NARCISSUS   PANSY

The aim of this exercise is not to become a botanist, but to help you become more familiar with flower names. It may take a little time to come up with all the answers, the Internet may help.

 # Floral Finds

A.

B.

C.

D.

E.

F.

G.

H.

I.

 # Floral Finds

J.

K.

L.

M.

N.

O.

P.

Q.

R.

Flights of Fancy

Using the pictures, match the birds with their names. The Internet may help you.

ALBATROSS	PUFFIN
FINCH	LARK
PLOVER	BUZZARD
PHEASANT	CRANE
PARTRIDGE	GROUSE
SWALLOW	HERON

You are not expected to be an ornithologist, but it is always helpful on tests to be familiar with different types of birds that may be referenced in verbal reasoning or comprehension questions.

Flights of Fancy

A.

B.

C.

D.

E.

F.

Flights of Fancy

G.

H.

I.

J.

K.

L.

HIDDEN AMONGST THE TREES

Find the 20 nouns that are types of trees.

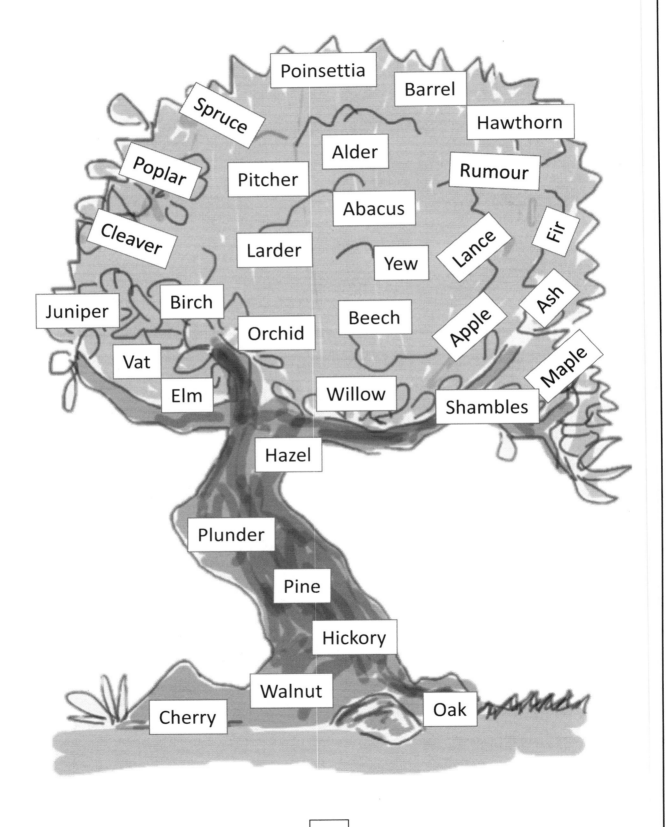

Being Instrumental

Where would you find these different instruments?

Concert Hall

Hospital

Factory

STETHOSCOPE	SOPRANO
VICE	SCALPEL
PICCOLO	ANVIL
TRIANGLE	SYRINGE
JIGSAW	PIPETTE
CASTANETS	PLIERS
FORCEPS	BASSOON
CHISEL	CYMBALS
VIOLIN	X-RAY
TIMPANI	VENTILATOR

Kooky Cartoons

USE THESE CARTOONS TO HELP YOU REMEMBER THE WORDS. CAN YOU DRAW SOME OF YOUR OWN TOO?

The turning bull was **turbulent**

The great ant allowed his army a holiday **(grant)**

The wind became little **(dwindle)**

Kooky Cartoons

Rob busted out of the jail with all his strength **(robust)**

Susie got full marks for the sums she did in mittens **(summit)**

Ana took a cab to the **cabana**

The orange pig meant it was a surprise to everyone **(pigment)**

This ram keeps ambling over the common **(ramble)**

Missing Word Sentences

Fill in the missing word using the words from the list:

Word List

ebb	frequent	caricatures
ceased	casual	guarantee
exterior	adversity	sleek
gullible	chaotic	economize
immense	scrawny	abandon
obvious	embezzled	assembled
fortunate	decay	

1) The crook had _____ a fortune before the detectives caught her.

2) The family needed to _____ as times were hard.

3) There is no _____ of safety at the water park, you must be careful.

4) The owner was very proud of his _____ new car.

5) The hockey player _____ competing because of his injury.

6) It was _____ that days were getting shorter as it was dark by 5:00 PM.

7) It is _____ in the train station as many passengers are waiting for delayed trains.

Missing Word Sentences

8) The campers had to _____ their tent because it had leaked during the storm.

9) Jill is very _____ and believes everything that her friends tell her.

10) Tooth _____ can cause serious health problems.

11) To overcome _____, you must face up to your challenges

12) The _____ and flow of the tide is very relaxing.

13) The _____ of the house was more beautiful than the interior.

14) Dean is a _____ visitor to the cinema as he loves films.

15) Freda is good at drawing cartoons and her _____ are very funny.

16) The king was thin and _____, but the people loved him.

17) Noah was _____ to be picked for the team.

18) The School _____ in the hall.

19) It was with _____ pride that the team held up the winners' trophy.

20) The man is wearing _____ clothes; jeans, a T-Shirt, and trainers.

FAKE NEWS

Discover what really happened. Replace the underlined words in the sentences with the antonyms from the list below:

OVERJOYED	PROGRESSION	ADMIRED
ENDANGERED	THWARTED	ORIGINAL
TIDY	DUSK	SUMMIT
LOYALTY	PARAMOUNT	ANXIOUS
PRAISED	SURPLUS	DECEITFUL

1) The <u>replica</u> painting was stolen by the <u>honest</u> trickster.

2) The <u>safe</u> animals were <u>confident</u> on the journey home.

3) <u>Betrayal</u> was something the mayor <u>despised</u>.

4) Failing in the driving test was of <u>least</u> importance to Charles.

5) Tom's <u>unkempt</u> bedroom made his father <u>distraught</u>.

6) The snow <u>increased</u> the climbers chances of reaching the <u>nadir</u> of the mountain

7) The coach <u>scolded</u> the football player for <u>regression</u> in his dribbling.

8) There was a <u>dearth</u> of bananas in the market at <u>dawn</u>.

Nonsense Poetry

Can you make sense of this poetry?

Can a dual have two fighters, one against another?

Do we enjoy desert left alone?

Do cops in a forest really exist?

Can a flea get away on its own?

What did the bald baby crying do?

Take a cue and wait for a while?

Can a tree take a bow, or a colonel a nut?

Feet may outperform if they hop for a mile

Can a tropical tree stand in the hand?

A friendly drink would be nice

Does a harp keep chattering on and on?

Let's not die, let's dice!

STORY BUILDER

A fun game for two players. Each player has a list of 20 words.

In this exercise, you will create a story based on a sentence from the previous player.

You must use at least one of the words in your list in each sentence.

Use only one connective word (AND, OR, ALSO, BUT) per sentence.

The winner is the first player to use all of their words, although this activity is really about working together.

LIST 1

shabby	modern
delayed	sketch
fret	labyrinth
nimble	agile
hinder	charge
roast	blank
trickle	succeed
minor	major
favour	assist
cob	navy

STORY BUILDER	STORY BUILDER
STORY BUILDER	STORY BUILDER
STORY BUILDER	STORY BUILDER
STORY BUILDER	STORY BUILDER
STORY BUILDER	STORY BUILDER
STORY BUILDER	STORY BUILDER
STORY BUILDER	STORY BUILDER
STORY BUILDER	STORY BUILDER
STORY BUILDER	STORY BUILDER

LIST 2

primary	intercept
fiction	resemble
kin	tolerate
unruly	internal
grave	confidential
ancestor	sullen
solemn	opponent
zenith	inquire
defy	pliable
contradict	unravel

STORY BUILDER	STORY BUILDER
STORY BUILDER	STORY BUILDER
STORY BUILDER	STORY BUILDER
STORY BUILDER	STORY BUILDER
STORY BUILDER	STORY BUILDER
STORY BUILDER	STORY BUILDER
STORY BUILDER	STORY BUILDER
STORY BUILDER	STORY BUILDER
STORY BUILDER	STORY BUILDER
STORY BUILDER	STORY BUILDER

QUACK QUACK

Find where the missing words go in the following excerpt from Beatrix Potter's classic story *The Tale of Jemima Puddle Duck.*

skimmed	waddle	shawl	civil
brood	suffocating	bonnet	alighted
escorted	patience	fowl	dismal
curiously	permitted	elegantly	quantity
suspicious	alarmed	pattering	pails
convenient	residence	dry	

What a funny sight it is to see a ____1____ of ducklings with a hen! Listen to the story of Jemima Puddle-duck, who was annoyed because the farmer's wife would not let her hatch her own eggs.

Her sister-in-law, Mrs. Rebeccah Puddle-duck, was perfectly willing to leave the hatchling to someone else – "I have not the ____2____ to sit on a nest for twenty-eight days; and no more have you, Jemima. You would let them go cold; you know you would!"

"I wish to hatch my own eggs; I will hatch them all by myself," quacked Jemima Puddle-duck. She tried to hide her eggs; but they were always found and carried off.

Jemima Puddle-duck became quite desperate. She determined to make a nest right away from the farm.

She set off on a fine spring afternoon along the cart-road that leads over the hill. She was wearing a shawl and a poke bonnet.

When she reached the top of the hill, she saw a wood in the distance. She thought that it looked a safe quiet spot.

QUACK QUACK

Jemima Puddle-duck was not much in the habit of flying. She ran downhill a few yards flapping her __3__, and then she jumped off into the air. She flew beautifully when she had gotten a good start.

She __4__ along over the treetops until she saw an open place in the middle of the wood, where the trees and brushwood had been cleared. Jemima __5__ rather heavily and began to __6__ about in search of a convenient dry nesting place. She rather fancied a tree stump amongst some tall foxgloves.

But – seated upon the stump, she was startled to find an __7__ dressed gentleman reading a newspaper. He had black prick ears and sandy coloured whiskers.

"Quack?" said Jemima Puddle-duck, with her head and her __8__ on the one side – "Quack?"

The gentleman raised his eyes above his newspaper and looked curiously at Jemima. "Madam, have you lost your way?" said he. He had a long bushy tail which he was sitting upon, as the stump was somewhat damp.

Jemima thought him mighty __9__ and handsome. She explained that she had not lost her way, but that she was trying to find a convenient __10__ nesting place.

"Ah! Is that so? Indeed!" said the gentleman with sandy whiskers, looking __11__ at Jemima. He folded up the newspaper, and put it in his coat-tail pocket.

Jemima complained of the superfluous hen.

"Indeed! How interesting! I wish I could meet with that __12__. I would teach it to mind its own business!"

QUACK QUACK

"But as to a nest – there is no difficulty; I have a sackful of feathers in my woodshed. No, my dear madam, you will be in nobody's way. You may sit there as long as you like," said the bushy long-tailed gentleman.

He led the long way to a very retired, ___13___-looking house amongst the fox-gloves.

It was built of faggots and turf, and there were two broken ___14___, one on top of another, by way of a chimney.

"This is my summer ___15___; you would not find my earth – my winter house – so ___16___," said the hospitable gentleman.

There was a tumbledown shed at the back of the house, made of old soap boxes. The gentleman opened the door, and showed Jemima in.

The shed was almost quite full of feathers – it was almost ___17___; but it was comfortable and very soft.

Jemima Puddle-duck was rather surprised to find such a vast ___18___ of feathers. But it was very comfortable; and she made a nest without any trouble at all..

Kidnapped Words!

Read the following passages from Robert Louis Stevenson's famous novels *Kidnapped* and *Treasure Island*. Some of the words have been "kidnapped" and used in the sentences afterward. Can you find the right words?

* * * * * *

Kidnapped

I will begin the story of my adventures with a certain morning early in the month of June, the year of grace 1751, when I took the key for the last time out of the door of my father's house. The sun began to shine upon the **summit** of the hills as I went down the road; and by the time I had come as far as the **manse**, the blackbirds were whistling in the garden lilacs, and the mist that hung around the valley in the time of the dawn was beginning to arise and die away.

Mr. Campbell, the minister of Essendean, was waiting for me by the garden gate, good man! He asked me if I had breakfasted; and hearing that I lacked for nothing, he took my hand in both of his and clapped it kindly under his arm.

"Well, Davie, lad," said he, "I will go with you as far as the **ford**, to set you on the way." And we began to walk forward in silence.

"Are ye sorry to leave Essendean?" said he, after awhile.

"Why, sir," said I, "if I knew where I was going, or what was likely to become of me, I would tell you **candidly**. Essendean is a good place indeed, and I have been very happy there; but then I have never been anywhere else. My father and mother, since they are both dead, I shall be no nearer to in Essendean than in the Kingdom of Hungary, and, to speak truth, if I thought I had a chance to better myself where I was going I would go with a good will."

"Ay?" said Mr. Campbell. "Very well, Davie. Then it behoves me to tell your fortune; or so far as I may. When your mother was gone, and your father (the worthy, Christian man) began to sicken for his end, he gave me in **charge** a certain letter, which he said was your **inheritance**. 'So soon,' says he, 'as I am gone, and the house is redd up (tidied up) and the gear **disposed** of' (all which, Davie, hath been done), 'give my boy this letter into his hand, and start him off to the house of Shaws, not far from Cramond. That is the place I came from,' he said, 'and it's where it befits that my boy should return. He is a steady lad,' your father said, 'and a **canny** goer; and I doubt not he will come safe, and be well lived where he goes.'"

Kidnapped Words!

* * * * * *

Treasure Island

Squire Trelawney, Dr. Livesey, and the rest of these gentlemen having asked me to write down the whole particulars about Treasure Island, from the beginning to the end, keeping nothing back but the **bearings** of the island, and that only because there is still treasure not yet lifted, I take up my pen in the year of grace 17— and go back to the time when my father kept the Admiral Benbow inn and the brown old seaman with the **sabre** cut first took up his lodging under our roof.

I remember him as if it were yesterday, as he came **plodding** to the inn door, his sea-chest following behind him in a hand-barrow — a tall, strong, heavy, nut-brown man, his tarry pigtail falling over the shoulder of his soiled blue coat, his hands **ragged** and scarred, with black, broken nails, and the sabre cut across one cheek, a dirty, **livid** white. I remember him looking round the cover and whistling to himself as he did so, and then breaking out in that old sea-song that he sang so often afterwards:

Fifteen men on the dead man's chest — Yo-ho-ho, and a bottle of rum!

in the high, old **tottering** voice that seemed to have been tuned and broken at the capstan bars. Then he rapped on the door with a bit of stick like a handspike that he carried, and when my father appeared, called roughly for a glass of rum. This, when it was brought to him, he drank slowly, like a connoisseur, **lingering** on the taste and still looking about him at the cliffs and up at our signboard.

Kidnapped Words!

From *Kidnapped*:

1. The captain was in _____ of organising the team.
2. Thomas _____ of the can in the correct recycling bin.
3. Linda reached the _____ in no time.
4. The driving instructor needs to speak _____ to encourage the pupil to focus on his driving.
5. The priest lived in a _____ that had seen better days.
6. Molly waded across the _____ in her Wellington boots.
7. The young man received a huge _____ when his Aunt died.

From *Treasure Island*:

8. The baby was _____ before falling over.
9. Felix lost his _____ after twirling around in circles.
10. Jemma was _____ outside the café.
11. The army rattled their _____ before the battle.
12. She was _____ down the road as she was so tired.
13. Dad was worn _____ by the mischievous children.
14. Wendy was _____ because her sister had stolen her make-up

WORD BANK

SUMMIT	MANSE	FORD
CANDIDLY	CHARGE	INHERITANCE
DISPOSED	CANNY	TOTTERING
LINGERING	LIVID	RAGGED
PLODDING	BEARINGS	SABRES

Colloquial Expressions

How good are you at understanding colloquial expressions? These use informal phrases and slang to express ideas. Draw a line from each expression to the matching meanings below:

Lead up the garden path	(BE) EXPOSED
Let the cat out of the bag	REFRAIN
Get into hot water	SLUMBER
Smell a rat	COAX
Mind your Ps & Qs	BOAST
Hold one's tongue	PANICKED
Sling mud	DECEIVE
Have a feather in one's cap	TORRENTIAL
Have your heart in your mouth	RE-ESTABLISH
Take 40 winks	CONCEDE
Take the bull by the horns	NON-COMMITAL
Pull the wool over someone's eyes	PREDICAMENT
Turn over a new leaf	LIMIT
Sit on the fence	HOAX
Pull someone's leg	COURTESY
Blow one's own trumpet	SLANDER
Raining cats and dogs	REVEAL
Face the music	CONFRONT
Throw in the towel	DECORATED
Draw the line	SUSPICION

Whatever the Weather

This is a card game where you must try to match the word with the type of weather it is describing. Cut out the weather type words and sets of category cards.

The categories of weather are:

STORMY	RAINY/WET	SUNNY	DRY
HUMID	COLD	FOGGY	HOT
FOGGY	WINDY	DULL/CLOUDY	

Give a set of category cards to each player. Shuffle all the other cards and make a pile. Take it in turns taking a weather card from the pile.

The first player to get five cards matching to a single weather type wins.

Category: STORMY	Category: HUMID
Category: RAINY/WET	Category: SUNNY
Category: COLD	Category: FOGGY
Category: DULL/CLOUDY	Category: WINDY
Category: DRY	Category: HOT
Oppressive	Stifling
Dank	Sultry
Drizzle	Drenched
Sopping	Saturated
Bitter	Siberian

Whatever the weather	Whatever the weather
Whatever the weather	Whatever the weather
Whatever the weather	Whatever the weather
Whatever the weather	Whatever the weather
Whatever the weather	Whatever the weather
Whatever the weather	Whatever the weather
Whatever the weather	Whatever the weather
Whatever the weather	Whatever the weather
Whatever the weather	Whatever the weather
Whatever the weather	Whatever the weather

Crisp	Glacial
Piercing	Polar
Pea Soup	Misty
Indistinct	Nebulous
Smog	Grey
Dismal	Gloomy
Overcast	Murky
Dreary	Bleak
Gusty	Blustery
Windswept	draughty

Whatever the weather	Whatever the weather
Whatever the weather	Whatever the weather
Whatever the weather	Whatever the weather
Whatever the weather	Whatever the weather
Whatever the weather	Whatever the weather
Whatever the weather	Whatever the weather
Whatever the weather	Whatever the weather
Whatever the weather	Whatever the weather
Whatever the weather	Whatever the weather
Whatever the weather	Whatever the weather

Brisk	Arid
Parched	Drought
Shrivelled	Baked
Tempestuous	Turbulent
Raging	Menacing
Luminous	Radiant
Pleasant	Brilliant
Beaming	Muggy

Whatever the weather	Whatever the weather
Whatever the weather	Whatever the weather
Whatever the weather	Whatever the weather
Whatever the weather	Whatever the weather
Whatever the weather	Whatever the weather
Whatever the weather	Whatever the weather
Whatever the weather	Whatever the weather
Whatever the weather	Whatever the weather

What was the Question??

This is an exercise where you are given an answer, but have to come up with a question. There may be more than one correct question for each answer.

Example: acorns
Possible Answer: What grows on an oak tree?

1. infantile
2. canine
3. estuary
4. brood
5. suede
6. cackle
7. flint
8. deceased
9. plume
10. replicate
11. dusk
12. qualm
13. tact
14. rigid
15. gallant
16. dictator
17. bunting
18. errand
19. aid
20. scoff

Sum It Up

The object of this game is to create words by combining two cards.

in	-side

Cut out the cards, and shuffle them. Each player takes two cards – do not show your cards to the other player(s). All of the other cards should go into a pile face down.

Players take turns drawing a new card.

If a player draws a card and cannot create a word, they should place one of their cards back under the pile. Then the next player takes a turn.

If the player draws a card that can be combined with one of their other cards to create a word, then the player gets a point and sets those cards aside. They should then draw one more card, and let the next player take a turn.

The player with the most completed words wins.

am	-bush
ab	-stain
am	-icable
en	-dure
en	-danger
ab	-olish
ab	-sent
as	-pect
as	-pire
in	-ferno

Sum It Up	Sum It Up
Sum It Up	Sum It Up
Sum It Up	Sum It Up
Sum It Up	Sum It Up
Sum It Up	Sum It Up
Sum It Up	Sum It Up
Sum It Up	Sum It Up
Sum It Up	Sum It Up
Sum It Up	Sum It Up
Sum It Up	Sum It Up

am	-phibian
in	-dulge
car	-go
car	-bon
in	-scribe
am	-ulet
in	-sure
as	-cend

Sum It Up	Sum It Up
Sum It Up	Sum It Up
Sum It Up	Sum It Up
Sum It Up	Sum It Up
Sum It Up	Sum It Up
Sum It Up	Sum It Up
Sum It Up	Sum It Up
Sum It Up	Sum It Up

ANALOGIES

Use your growing vocabulary knowledge to match the analogies. The second pair of words will match in the same way as the first by picking from the choices given.

Example:
nib : pen   lens : frame / focus / (telescope) / glass / stars

1. colour : spectrum   waves : rock / beach / lap / sound / dolphin

2. angels : host   ship : flock / bunch / cast / tribe / flotilla

3. horse : equine   cat : mouse / bovine / piscine / elephantine / feline

4. seven : nine   twelve : eighteen / fourteen / ten / five / twenty

5. hyena : screams   monkey : talks / swing / chatters / ape / banana

6. quay : key   raise : lift / above / rays / earn / wealth

7. tranquil : peaceful   stop : adopt / surprise / prohibit / accept / alter

8. impatient : patient   brisk : leisurely / easily / quickly / definitely / wisely

9. methodical : organised   rupture : harm / hurt / break / mend / fix

10. diplomatic : tactful   lucid : clever / hard / comprehensible / tricky / wide

11. crucial : unnecessary   heavy : large / bulky / light / thick / burdensome

12. strife : peace   wide : long / fat / thick / narrow / sharp

13. chatter : talk   ballet : pirouette / tap / shoes / dance / leotard

14. burgundy : red   purple : white / blue / orange / green / yellow

15. 10 : decade   1000 : year / century / millennium / thousand / time

16. rabbit : warren   badger : bed / dam / sett / hive / nest

17. brass : cornet   string : pipe / tuba / harp / clarinet / drum

MADDENING MISSING LETTERS

Read the passage from *Alice's Adventures in Wonderland* by Lewis Carroll. After the reading, fill in the missing letters of the highlighted words.

* * * * *

The table was a large one, but the three were all crowded together at one corner of it: `No room! No room!' they cried out when they saw Alice coming. `There's **P_EN_Y** of room!' said Alice **ind_g_ant_y**, and she sat down in a large arm-chair at one end of the table.

`Have some wine,' the March Hare said in an encouraging tone.

Alice looked all round the table, but there was nothing on it but tea. `I don't see any wine,' she **r_mar_ed**.

`There isn't any,' said the March Hare.

`Then it wasn't very **c_v_l** of you to offer it,' said Alice angrily.

`It wasn't very civil of you to sit down without being **i_vi_ed**,' said the March Hare.

`I didn't know it was YOUR table,' said Alice; `it's laid for a great many more than three.'

`Your hair wants cutting,' said the Hatter. He had been looking at Alice for some time with great **c_ri_s_ty**, and this was his first **s_eec_**.

`You should learn not to make **p_rs_nal** remarks,' Alice said with some severity; `it's very rude.'

The Hatter opened his eyes very wide on hearing this; but all he SAID was, `Why is a raven like a writing-desk?'

`Come, we shall have some fun now!' thought Alice. `I'm glad they've begun asking **r_ddl_s**.–I believe I can guess that,' she added **al_u_**.

MADDENING MISSING LETTERS

`Do you mean that you think you can find out the answer to it?' said the March Hare.

`Exactly so,' said Alice.

`Then you should say what you mean,' the March Hare went on.

`I do,' Alice **h s ily** replied; `at least–at least I mean what I say–that's the same thing, you know.'

Not the same thing a bit!' said the Hatter. `You might just as well say that "I see what I eat" is the same thing as "I eat what I see"!'

`You might just as well say,' added the March Hare, `that "I like what I get" is the same **t i g** as "I get what I like"!'

`You might just as well say,' added the Dormouse, who seemed to be **w  lki  g** in his sleep, `that "I breathe when I sleep" is the same thing as "I sleep when I breathe"!'

`It IS the same thing with you,' said the Hatter, and here the **co v rsa io** dropped, and the party sat silent for a ** in t** , while Alice thought over all she could remember about ravens and writing-desks, which wasn't much.

The Hatter was the first to break the **s lenc** . `What day of the month is it?' he said, turning to Alice: he had taken his watch out of his pocket, and was looking at it uneasily, **h k n** it every now and then, and holding it to his ear.

Alice considered a little, and then said `The **fo rth**.'

`Two days wrong!' sighed the Hatter. `I told you butter wouldn't suit the works!' he added looking **a g il** at the March Hare.

`It was the BEST **u t r**,' the March Hare meekly replied.

Snap!

Cut out the cards on the following pages. All cards should be shuffled and placed in a central pile face down. The players take turns lifting up a card, placing it face up so that all can see, creating a row of cards.

If a card is lifted from the main stack of cards, that is the same word as one of any of the cards already lifted, the first player to say "Snap!" and to give two different meanings of the word, gets to keep that pair of cards.

Example:

WIND – a gust of air
WIND – to turn

The winner is the player with the most pairs of cards after all cards have been lifted.

ball	ball
bear	bear
boot	boot
case	case
counter	counter
dash	dash
duck	duck
firm	firm
jam	jam
lap	lap

Snap!	Snap!
Snap!	Snap!
Snap!	Snap!
Snap!	Snap!
Snap!	Snap!
Snap!	Snap!
Snap!	Snap!
Snap!	Snap!
Snap!	Snap!
Snap!	Snap!

bat	bat
boil	boil
bowl	bowl
club	club
cricket	cricket
date	date
fair	fair
flat	flat
key	key
light	light

Snap!	Snap!
Snap!	Snap!
Snap!	Snap!
Snap!	Snap!
Snap!	Snap!
Snap!	Snap!
Snap!	Snap!
Snap!	Snap!
Snap!	Snap!
Snap!	Snap!

match	match
might	might
organ	organ
pride	pride
ram	ram
row	row
shed	shed
spring	spring
staff	staff
tip	tip

Snap!	Snap!
Snap!	Snap!
Snap!	Snap!
Snap!	Snap!
Snap!	Snap!
Snap!	Snap!
Snap!	Snap!
Snap!	Snap!
Snap!	Snap!
Snap!	Snap!

mean	mean
mind	mind
palm	palm
pupil	pupil
rock	rock
seal	seal
spell	spell
squash	squash
stick	stick
top	top

Snap!	Snap!
Snap!	Snap!
Snap!	Snap!
Snap!	Snap!
Snap!	Snap!
Snap!	Snap!
Snap!	Snap!
Snap!	Snap!
Snap!	Snap!
Snap!	Snap!

Professionally Speaking

Can you identify what these people do? The professions have been specifically selected because they have been used in past Eleven Plus questions. Match the profession on the left with what they do on the right column.

PHYSICIAN	Makes maps
PHARMACIST	Studies the economy
ENGINEER	Makes arrangements at a funeral
ARCHAEOLOGIST	Sells houses and property
ARCHITECT	Handles and carries luggage
CARTOGRAPHER	Doctor
STONEMASON	Greets clients at an office
DIETICIAN	Digs up and studies artefacts
ECONOMIST	Fixes leaks
UNDERTAKER	Makes or sells women's hats
FARRIER	Designs machines or structures
GLAZIER	Designs buildings
PORTER	Helps to straighten teeth
RECEPTIONIST	Provides emergency medical care
MILLINER	Practises law in a court
MINER	Makes and repairs clothing
ORTHODONTIST	Dispenses medicine
PARAMEDIC	Fits glass into windows and doors
PLUMBER	Makes and repairs things in iron
BARRISTER	Cuts, prepares and builds with stone
TAILOR	Makes and repairs wooden objects
ESTATE AGENT	Expert on diet and nutrition
BLACKSMITH	Works in a mine
CARPENTER	Makes shoes for horses

You're Breaking Up

This section features words that have been broken up into pictures. This can help you remember some tricky words.

<u>Clue</u>

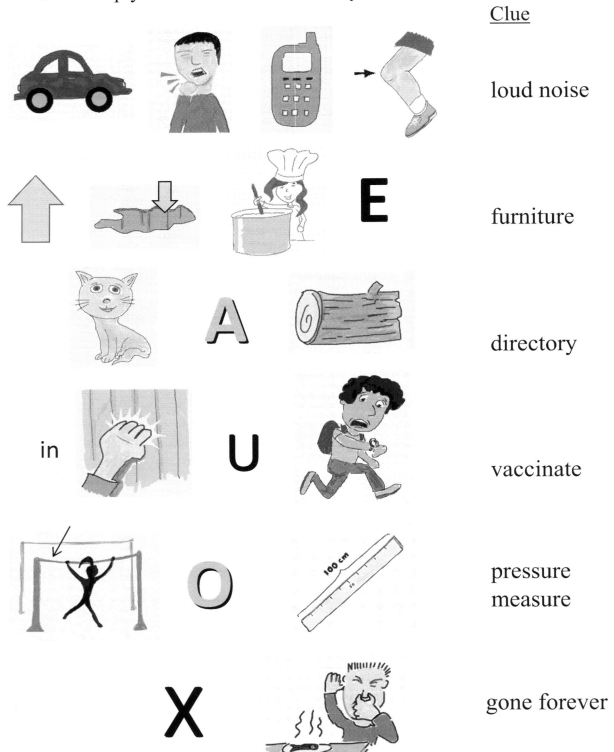

loud noise

furniture

directory

vaccinate

pressure
measure

gone forever

You're Breaking Up

  material

  no re-print

  floating

  in your head

  optimistic

SQUARE ROOTS

This is a game that will assist you in learning common root words. It will help you to work out many more unfamiliar terms. Before you begin, spend some time looking at the root words and their meanings on page 140.

How to play: Cut out the cards, shuffle them and place them in a pile. Use the dot grid.

Players take turns drawing cards. If they can correctly provide the meaning of the root word on the card, then they can draw a line joining two dots on the grid.

As in the traditional game of squares, players attempt to complete a square and write their initial inside.

There are 20 root words on the cards. Once all of the cards have been used, shuffle them and start again until the grid has been completely filled with squares.

The winner will have completed the most squares.

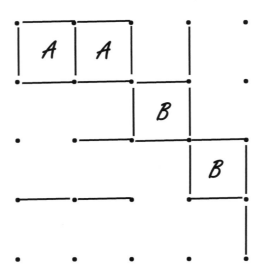

AUDIO	CHROMO
POLY	PHOTO
SPHERE	BIO
GEO	LOGO
PHONE	SCOPE
MAL	BEN
BI	HYPER
HYPO	ANTI
ANTE	SUB
SYN	UNI

SQUARE ROOTS	SQUARE ROOTS
SQUARE ROOTS	SQUARE ROOTS
SQUARE ROOTS	SQUARE ROOTS
SQUARE ROOTS	SQUARE ROOTS
SQUARE ROOTS	SQUARE ROOTS
SQUARE ROOTS	SQUARE ROOTS
SQUARE ROOTS	SQUARE ROOTS
SQUARE ROOTS	SQUARE ROOTS
SQUARE ROOTS	SQUARE ROOTS
SQUARE ROOTS	SQUARE ROOTS

Square Roots

ROOT WORD MEANINGS

MAL – bad

HYPER – over

BIO – life

PHOTO – light

BI – two

CHROMO – colour

UNI – one

GEO – earth

POLY – many

ANTI – against

BEN – good

SYN – same

PHONE – sound

SPHERE – ball

ANTE – before

HYPO – under

LOGO – word/reason

AUDIO – hear

SCOPE – see

SUB – under

Square Roots

GAME GRID

Square Roots

GAME GRID

FAMOUS ANAGRAMS

There are some very famous scientists and inventors that have touched our lives so notably that they have even found their way into the Eleven Plus! A basic general knowledge about these figures is well worth knowing.

See if you can unscramble the letters and determine which famous person's name is given. There is a clue for each name. Feel free to use the Answer Key at the back of the book.

Example:

          E   L
    L   B

= BELL (Alexander Graham Bell, inventor of the telephone)

1) Hint: Star Man

2) Hint: Computer

3) Hint: Bible printer

4) Hint: Helped us see at night

FAMOUS ANAGRAMS

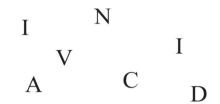

5) Hint: Brief History of Time

6) Hint: All-rounder

L B
L I
E R A

P
R T U
S E A

7) Hint: Read without seeing

8) Hint: Milking it

W E
T O
N N

U I
R
E C

9) Hint: The apple falls

10) Hint: Radioactive

S
R E
O M

N W I
R
A D

11) Hint: Code

12) Hint: Evolved

Noughts and Crosses

This game is designed to be used as revision close to the exam. It can either be played as a traditional game of noughts and crosses, or as extreme noughts and crosses.

In the regular version, players take turns marking either an X or O in a single grid of nine squares. Before taking a turn, players are challenged to give a definition for any word in the glossary – only the opponent picks the word! If the player guessing can give the correct answer, then they can make a mark. The players try to win by getting three X's or O's in a row, horizontally, vertically or diagonally. The winner of the first four out of nine games will be champion.

The second version (extreme) demands a great deal of strategic thinking, which is very good for non-verbal reasoning. This version uses the whole sheet of nine games, not just a single grid at a time. As in the regular version, players take turns by giving a correct definition or synonym to a glossary word, chosen by their opponent. Players can mark their X or O in any square on the sheet.. In effect, you are playing nine games at once! The player who can win three individual grids horizontally, vertically, or diagonally wins the game (See example below).

The game sheets are on the next four pages.

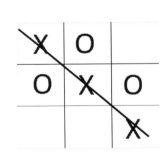

Crosses player winning
Regular version

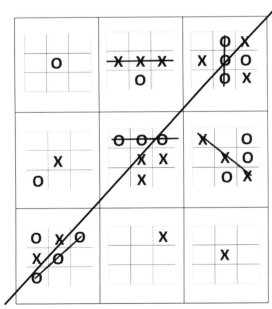

Noughts player winning
Extreme version

Noughts and Crosses

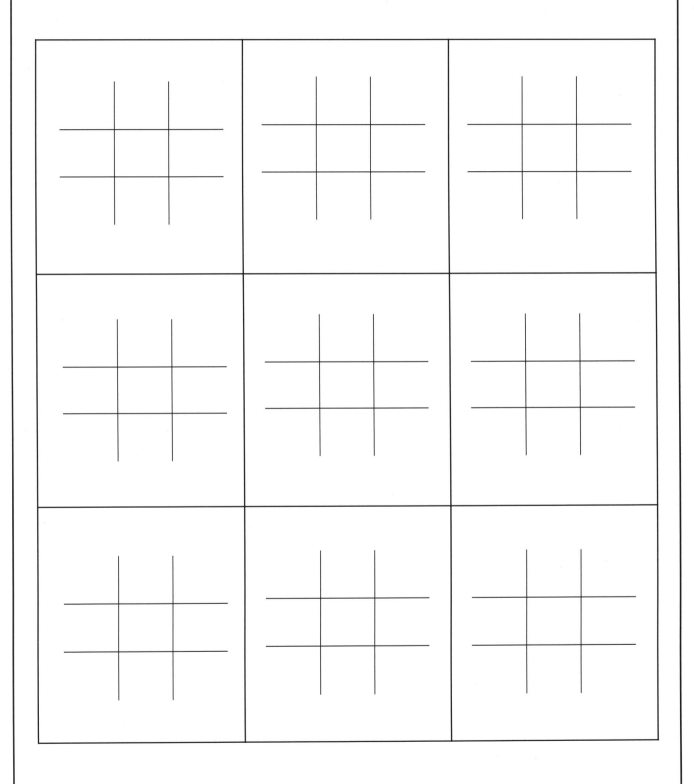

Noughts and Crosses

Noughts and Crosses

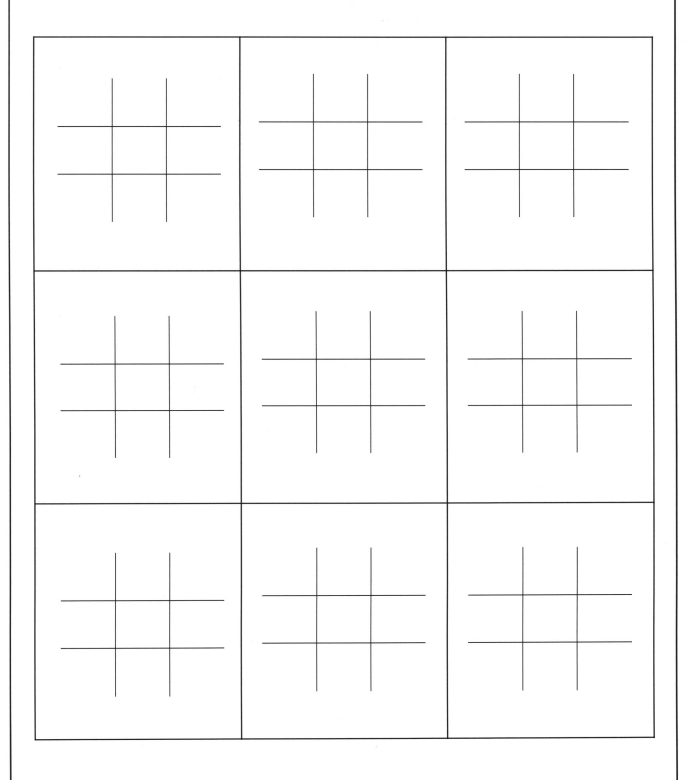

Noughts and Crosses

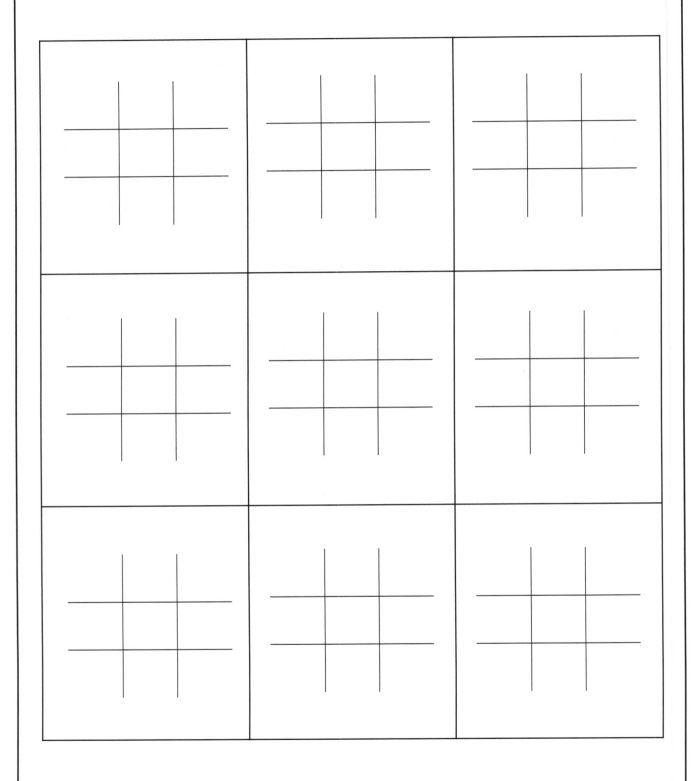

Glossary

Word	Definitions	Seen on Pages
abacus	*noun* - a simple counting tool that uses beads	87
abandon	*verb* - leave; give up on; *noun* - recklessness; without constraint	92
abhorrent	*adjective* - dreadful; hated; loathed; repugnant	20
abide	*verb* - accept; comply with; follow	26
abolish	*verb* - get rid of; put an to something	116
abrupt	*adjective* - sudden and unexpected; hurried; hasty	28
absent	*adjective* - not present; away	116
abstain	*verb* - to not do something, particularly something you enjoy	116
absurd	*adjective* - unreasonable; ridiculous	56, 61
abundance	*noun* - a large quantity of something; plenty	20
accelerate	*verb* - become faster; happen sooner	51
accept	*verb* - receive, welcome; agree to; believe; tolerate	57, 58, 120
achievement	*noun* - something done successfully, showing great skill and effort	28
acorn	*noun* - the nut that grows on an oak tree	114
acquire	*verb* - get, obtain, receive; learn or develop	10
acquisition	*noun* - the process of getting something; something that has been bought or received	74
active	*adjective* - energetic; lively; working, in operation	57, 63
acute	*adjective* - severe, critical; having an accurate sense in differences; an angle of less than 90 degrees	75
admire	*verb* - praise, respect, be impressed with	77, 93
adapt	*verb* - make something work for a new purpose; change to work in a new place or conditions	80
adopt	*verb* - take on; choose; take a child legally into your family	120
adroit	*adjective* - quick and skilful	75
adversity	*noun* - difficulty; an unpleasant situation	31, 92
advocate	*verb* - publicly support or recommend an idea; *noun* - someone who publicly supports something; a lawyer who defends someone in court	63
affable	*adjective* - friendly, pleasant; amiable; genial	15, 17, 69
affluent	*adjective* - wealthy	15
agile	*adjective* - nimble, can move with ease	15, 22, 54, 96
agitated	*adjective* - annoyed, disturbed	15, 57
aid	*noun* - help provided, assistance; verb - help, support	21, 114
ajar	*adjective* - slightly open	54, 61
alarmed	*adjective* - scared or worried about something	100
albatross	*noun* - a white large sea bird; something or someone that is causing you problems	84
alder	*noun* - a tree of the birch family, usually found near rivers or lakes	87
alight	*verb* - leave by taking a step down (i.e. alighted the bus); descend from the air and settle (bird); *adjective* - on fire; shining brightly	100
allocate	*verb* - give someone a share of something	78
aloud	*adverb* - out loud, not in a whisper	121
alter	*verb* - change	120
amass	*verb* - collect or gather a large amount of something over time	21
amber	*noun* - a fossil from tree resin, used frequently in jewellery; a honey-yellow colour; light used as a caution between green and red on a traffic signal	76
ambush	*verb* - attack from a hidden place; *noun* - collective noun for tigers	38, 116

Word	Definitions	Seen on Pages
amethyst	*noun* - a precious purple stone; a violet or purple colour	76
amiable	*adjective* - friendly and easy going	17
amicable	*adjective* - friendly, good-natured	116
amphibian	*noun* - an animal that can live on land or in the water	4, 21, 118
amulet	*noun* - a lucky charm or object worn as protection against evil or danger	118
ancestor	*noun* - someone genetically related from the distant past	98
anchor	*noun* - a heavy object on a chain used to keep a ship from moving at sea; something or someone who provides stability or gives support when needed	26
angel	*noun* - a heavenly being; a person of exceptional virtue	38, 120
angrily	*adverb* - acting in a behaviour showing anger; threatening	122
annihilate	*verb* - completely destroy	64
anonymous	*adjective* - not known by name	80
ante (root)	before	136, 138
anthology	*noun* - a collection of writings by different authors in a single book	33
anti (root)	against	136, 138
antonym	*noun* - a word that has the opposite meaning as another word	7, 55, 93
anvil	*noun* - a heavy iron block, used for shaping metal	88
anxious	*adjective* - worried, concerned; eager, keen	93
appalled	*adjective* - shocked; disgusted	21
arch	*noun* - a curved structure that supports weight (as in a bridge or doorway); a shape with a curved, symmetrical line; the curved underside of the foot	66
archaeologist	*noun* - a person that studies the past by examining objects	132
architect	*noun* - a person that designs and builds	132
arid	*adjective* - dry; having little or no rain	8, 72, 112
armoire	*noun* - a cupboard or wardrobe	33
army	*noun* - a military force that fights on land; a very large group of people; collective noun for a group of ants	38
arrogant	*adjective* - having an exaggerated opinion of oneself; conceited; vain	17, 77
arsenal	*noun* - a place where guns and weapons are stored	38
artificial	*adjective* - not real, fake; not sincere	72
ascend	*verb* - go up; climb	47, 48, 118
ascent	*noun* - a journey to the top of something; a path to the top; the movement of something up in the air	60
ash	*noun* - the left-over residue of something that has burned; a type of tree that provides hard, pale wood used in making furniture, cabinets and floors	87
aspect	*noun* – a part or feature of something; a view or position of a building	116
aspire	*verb* - hope to achieve something	116
assemble	*verb* - join together; construct or set up	92
assist	*verb* - help; be present as a helper; noun - an act of providing help	96
assistant	*noun* - someone who helps with a job or function; a subordinate or deputy	64
astute	*adjective* - very intelligent and aware; shrewd	26
atrium	*noun* - a central hall in a building, usually with a glass ceiling	21
attainment	*noun* - the act of achieving something	28
attempt	*verb* - try to do something; noun - the action of trying to do something	72
aubergine	*noun* - a dark purple vegetable	21, 64
audio (root)	sound	136, 138
auspicious	*adjective* - promising; favourable	63, 75
aviary	*noun* - a large cage used to keep birds	21
avoid	*verb* - keep away from	54
awe	*noun* - amazement, admiration	31
awning	*noun* - material attached to a structure for protection against the sun and rain	4, 20

Word	Definitions	Seen on Pages
axes	*noun* - (plural of axe) a wood-cutting tool	40
axis	*noun* - a line around which a body rotates; a line used to show position; an agreement or alliance between two or more countries	40
azalea	*noun* - a plant or bush with brightly-coloured flowers, a type of rhododendron	81
azure	*noun* - a bright blue colour; adjective - have a bright blue colour, like the sky	76
Babbage	Charles Babbage (1791- 1871) English mathematician, inventor, who originated the idea of a computer	141
badger	*noun* - a nocturnal mammal with grey-brown fur and a black and white head; *verb* - to pester someone	120
baffle	*verb* - confuse, puzzle	56, 74
baguette	*noun* - a long stick of bread (French)	64
bake	*verb* - cook in an oven; become very hot (weather)	112
baking	*adjective* - heat at a high temperature	36
bald	*adjective* - without hair (usually referring to the head)	42, 94
ball	*noun* - a solid, round figure; a round object used in a sports game; a formal dance; *verb* - to squeeze or form something into a round shape	124
balmy	*adjective* - pleasantly warm	36
barometer	*noun* - an instrument to measure pressure	133
barrel	*noun* - a large container for liquids with a flat top and bottom; collective noun for laughs and monkeys	38, 87
barren	*adjective* - unable to produce vegetation; bleak and lifeless	11
barrister	*noun* - a lawyer that works in a high court	132
base	*noun* - bottom, or lowest part of something; foundation; headquarters; the main ingredient or element; *verb* - use as a foundation; locate as a main point of operations	40, 54
based	(past tense of base) *adjective* - where a person or group is centrally located	40
bashful	*adjective* - shy, easily embarrassed	17
bass	*noun* - male singer with the lowest singing voice; an instrument with the lowest pitch (example: bass guitar); a type of fish	40
bassoon	*noun* - a large woodwind instrument of the oboe family	88
baste	*verb* - pour hot fat or juices over meat whilst cooking	40
bat	*noun* - a nocturnal mammal that can fly; a stick used to hit a ball in some sports games; *verb* - to hit at something with a bat	126
bawl	*verb* - call out noisily; cry like a child	42, 94
beach	*noun* - a sandy place near the sea	44
beam	*verb* - transmit a signal; smile with a wide and happy grin; shine brightly	112
bear	*verb* - carry, transport; have, exhibit; support; endure, put up with; give birth to; *noun* - a large mammal with a thick fur coat	124
bearings	*noun* - an understanding of direction that tells you where you are	104, 105
bed	*noun* - a place to sleep; collective noun for oysters	38
beech	*noun* - a type of large tree, with smooth, grey bark	44, 87
Bell	Alexander Graham Bell (1847- 1922) Scottish-American inventor of the telephone	141
ben (root)	good	136, 138
benefit	*noun* – an advantage; profit; *verb* - receive an advantage; be helped by something	1
benign	*adjective* - harmless; gentle, kind	10
beret	*noun* - a flat felt hat, traditionally French	3, 33, 63
besiege	*verb* - surround and harass; overwhelm	21
betrayal	*noun* - an act of disloyalty, when others have believed you to be loyal	93
bewildered	*adjective* - baffled, confused	17
bi (root)	two	136, 138

Word	Definitions	Seen on Pages
bilingual	*noun* - a person that can speak two languages fluently	15
bio (root)	earth	136, 138
birch	*noun* - a type of tree with smooth, white bark	87
biting	*adjective* - bitterly cold; (of criticism) harsh	36
bitter	*adjective* - angry because of something that happened in the past; a sharp and unpleasant taste; very cold (weather)	108
blacklist	*noun* - a list of names regarded as unacceptable, and therefore should be avoided or excluded	21
blacksmith	*noun* - a person who works with metal to create or repair	132
blank	*adjective* - empty, with no information; showing no understanding or reaction	96
blanket	*noun* - a large, usually wool, cover for a bed; *adjective* - total and inclusive; *verb* - cover completely	73
bleak	*adjective* - dull, dismal (weather); depressing	110
blend	*verb* - mix; combine; *noun* - a mixture of different things	54
bloated	*adjective* - swollen, enlarged; excessive	59
blonde	*noun* - a light yellow colour, or a person with blonde hair	76
blush	*verb* - show shyness or embarrassment by getting red in the face; *noun* – reddening of the cheeks as a sign of embarrassment; a pink or pale red colour	76
blustery	*adjective* - very windy	110
boar	*noun* - a male pig	42
boast	*verb* - to show off; brag or have excessive pride	106
bolster	*verb* - to support or strengthen	10, 63
bonnet	*noun* - a type of hat that covers the ears and is tied under the chin; the part of a car that covers the engine	64, 100
boil	*verb* - heat a liquid until it starts to bubble and turn to a gas; cook food by boiling; be angry or furious; *noun* - temperature at which a liquid turns to gas; an inflamed swelling on the skin	126
boot	*noun* - footwear that covers the foot, ankle and lower leg; a hard kick; space in the back of a car where items can be stored; *verb* - kick something with the foot; start up a computer	124
bore	*verb* - make a hole in something; *noun* - someone or a situation that is dull; the hollow inside of a gun	42
bough	*noun* - a main branch of a tree	94
boundary	*noun* - a line which marks the limits of an area; perimeter, edge	74
buoyant	*adjective* - positive, cheerful; able to keep afloat	13, 134
bovine	*adjective* - relating to cows or cattle; *noun* - an animal of the group of cattle	4, 120
bow	*verb* - bend the body at the waist; *noun* - the movement of bending the head or body forward; the front of a ship; a knot tied with two loose ends, usually as a decoration; a weapon for shooting arrows; a thin piece of wood used to play a string instrument (violin, cello, etc.)	66, 94
bowl	*noun* - a round dish used to hold food or liquid; the rounded inside part of something; *verb* - roll a ball along the ground	126
bowler	*noun* - someone who throws a ball in a game of bowling or skittles; a cricket player who bowls; a type of man's hat with a round crown	64
Braille	Louis Braille (1809-1852) invented a system of reading and writing for the blind	142
brass	*noun* - a yellowish metal made of copper and zinc; people in authority; musical instruments made of metal and played by blowing into a mouthpiece (e.g. trumpet, trombone, tuba)	120
brilliant	*adjective* - clever, talented; very bright in colour; excellent	75, 112
brisk	*adjective* - active, energetic; quick, rapid; abrupt; crisp	112, 120
brogue	*noun* - a type of leather shoe; an accent when speaking English (Scottish, Irish)	63

Word	Definitions	Seen on Pages
brooch	*noun* - jewellery worn with a pin to hold it in place	33
brood	*noun* - a collection of birds or children; *verb* - to think for a long time in a negative way	100, 114
brunette	*noun* - a woman with dark brown hair; *adjective* - dark brown in colour	76
bulbous	*adjective* - large and round	3
bulky	*adjective* - difficult to carry due to size and shape	51
bunting	*noun* - row of small flags on a string, hung as decoration	114
burden	*noun* - something difficult to manage; a heavy load	20
burdensome	*adjective* - difficult to manage or accomplish	120
bureau	*noun* - a writing desk with drawers; an agency or department	33
burgundy	*noun* - a deep red colour; a type of wine from Burgundy (a region in France)	120
butter	*noun* - a yellow spreadable food made by churning cream	122
buzzard	*noun* - a large bird of prey that is a type of hawk	84
cabana	*noun* - a hut or cabin at a beach, or swimming pool	90
cackle	*noun* - a wicked laugh; *verb* - laugh in a loud, harsh way	60, 114
cacophony	*noun* - a loud collection of noises; racket; din	133
cajole	*verb* - persuade	69
callous	*adjective* - cruel, insensitive	42
callus	*noun* - a thick and hardened piece of skin	42
camouflage	*noun* - covering used to hide by blending into the background; *verb* - hide or conceal something by use of camouflage	73
candidly	*adverb* - honestly; in a straightforward way	103, 105
canine	*adjective* - relating to dogs; *noun* - a dog	4, 114
canny	*adjective* - shrewd and with good judgement; clever	103, 105
cantankerous	*adjective* - bad-tempered; irritable, grumpy	31
capable	*adjective* - having the ability to do something; competent; proficient	63
captive	*noun* - prisoner	47, 48
carbon	*noun* - a chemical element	118
cargo	*noun* - a load carried by land, sea or air	118
caricature	*noun* - a drawing or picture of someone with exaggerated features	92
carnation	*noun* - a flower, usually red, white, or pink in colour	81
carpenter	*noun* - a person that uses wood to make or repair things	132
cartographer	*noun* - a person who makes maps	132
case	*noun* - a situation or example; a matter to be decided by a court or other authorities; a container or box to store things in; an argument for something	124
cassette	*noun* - a plastic container that holds recorded music (or film) that is on tape	69
castanets	*noun* - a musical percussion instrument	88
casual	*adjective* - relaxed, informal; not taking much interest; not serious	92
catalogue	*noun* - a list of a collection of similar things	133
caution	*noun* - great care and attention; advice or a warning; *verb* - to warn someone	79
cease	*verb* - stop; end	8, 91
cellar	*noun* - basement	31
cent	*noun* - a small unit of money worth one hundredth of a dollar, Euro, etc.	42
centre	*noun* - the middle; a building or place where something takes place	53, 63
century	*noun* - 100 years	120
chaos	*noun* - complete disorder, confusion or mayhem	1
chaotic	*adjective* - completely disorganised and confused; in disarray	91
chaperone	*noun* - person that watches and protects another	21
charge	*verb* - ask for payment; accuse someone; assign a duty or responsibility; store energy in a battery; rush forward in attack; *noun* - a price; fee; accusation; responsibility for the care of something; energy stored; an attack or assault	96, 103, 105

Word	Definitions	Seen on Pages
charmed	*adjective* - unusually lucky	75
chartreuse	*noun* - a pale yellow or green colour	76
chastise	*verb* - scold, reprimand, admonish	8
chatter	*verb* - talk informally; short, high-pitched sounds made by monkeys, etc.	120
cheat	*verb* - act unfairly to get what you want; break the rules; *noun* – someone who is dishonest	1
cheerful	*adjective* - happy and positive, optimistic	17
cherish	*verb* - protect and care; treasure	47, 48
cherry	*noun* - a small, round, red fruit that grows on a cherry tree; the tree that bears the cherry fruit; a deep red colour	87
chevron	*noun* - An V-shaped line or stripe, used to signify rank in the military	4
chief	*noun* - leader of a group; highest-ranking person; *adjective* - lead; most important	64
chilly	*adjective* - unpleasantly cold; unfriendly	36
chisel	*noun* - small tool used for shaping wood, stone or metal	28, 64, 88
choir	*noun* - a singing group	77
chord	*noun* - a group of musical notes played at the same time	26, 42
chromo (root)	colour	136, 138
chrysanthemum	*noun* - a colourful flower related to the daisy	81
chute	*noun* - a long tube; passage	44
civil	*adjective* - relating to ordinary citizens, members of a community; courteous and polite	100, 121
clarify	*verb* - make clear	21, 63
clarinet	*noun* - a woodwind instrument that is tube-shaped and played with a single reed mouthpiece	120
cleaver	*noun* - cutting tool, typically used by a butcher to chop meat	50, 87
clement	*adjective* - pleasant (describing weather)	36
clever	*adjective* - intelligent, smart; skilful	25, 75, 120
cloak	*verb* - cover, mask; *noun* - an overgarment	73
close	*adjective* - near, not far from; not open; stifling, humid (weather); having a good relationship; careful; *verb* - change from being open to not open; to end something	36, 64
club	*noun* - an organization or group; a place used by a group of people for an activity	126
clutch	*verb* - to hold tightly; *noun* - device in a vehicle that connects and disconnects the engine and transmission system; a group of eggs	38
coarse	*adjective* - rough	20, 58, 69
coax	*verb* - persuade someone gently to do something	1, 106
cob	*noun* - a strong horse with short legs; a male swan; a small loaf of bread	96
colonel	*noun* - a high military officer rank in the army or air force	94
combine	*verb* - mix; join, unite, get together	54
commence	*verb* - begin, start; launch	73
commend	*verb* - praise, compliment, congratulate	10
compass	*noun* - instrument for measuring direction	20
complete	*adjective* - total, all; *verb* - finish making or doing something	72, 73
complicate	*verb* - make difficult	72
comprehensible	*adjective* - understandable	120
comprehensive	*adjective* - all-inclusive; complete; a school for children of all abilities above the age of eleven	73
conceal	*verb* - hide, keep out of sight; prevent from being known	61, 73, 77
concede	*verb* - admit to something; give away or allow someone to have something	106

Word	Definitions	Seen on Pages
conceited	*adjective* - vain, overly proud of oneself	17
condemn	*verb* - strongly criticise; denounce	20
condiment	*noun* - an item (such as salt, pepper or mustard) that can enhance the flavour of food	20
confident	*adjective* - being assured of one's abilities; feeling certain or optimistic	93
confidential	*adjective* - private; secret	59, 98
confound	*verb* - completely confuse, by being difficult to explain or deal with	57
confront	*verb* - stand up to someone; challenge; deal with something directly	106
confuse	*verb* - perplex, confound; complicate; identify wrongly, mistake	74
consideration	*noun* - serious thought; a fact taken in account when deciding something; payment or fee	79
constable	*noun* - a police officer	4
constant	*adjective* - frequent; unchanging	56, 63
constrict	*verb* - make narrower; squeeze; restrict	78
contact	*noun* - touch; a type of glasses worn directly on the eye; communication; acquaintance; *verb* - communicate with; touch someone or something	64
contemporary	*adjective* - current, modern, up-to date; noun - a person living at the same time as another	20, 54
contradict	*verb* - deny by claiming the opposite; challenge; be in conflict with	98
conundrum	*noun* - a hard puzzle; a difficult and confusing problem	74
convenient	*adjective* - fits well with your needs; involving little trouble or effort; within easy reach	100
convent	*noun* - a nun's home	69
conversation	*noun* - a discussion, between two or more people	122
cop	*noun* - a police officer	94
copse	*noun* - a small group of trees	94
copyright	*noun* - a legal right that protects work from being copied	134
cord	*noun* - string, rope; ribbed fabric (esp. trousers)	42, 57
cordial	*adjective* - friendly, amiable; noun - a sweet fruit-flavoured drink	10, 61, 94
cornet	*noun* - a brass instrument that looks like a trumpet only smaller; an ice cream cone	120
costly	*adjective* - very expensive; involving a lot of loss or damage	75
cotton	*noun* - plant that provides the fibre to make thread and textiles; the thread made from cotton	63
counter	*noun* - a long, flat surface in a business or home where people are served; a device or person that counts; a marker used in a game; *verb* - speak in opposition to something; adverb - in a way that opposes something	124
courageous	*adjective* - not afraid of danger or pain; brave	15
courtesy	*noun* - politeness, good manners	106
cover	*verb* - put something over another thing to protect or hide it; extend over an area; travel; report on; pay for something; disguise or conceal	73
coy	*adjective* - shy, modest; reluctant to give information	26
craggy	*adjective* - rocky and uneven, rough	60
crane	*noun* - a metal structure used to lift and move heavy objects; a tall bird with a long legs and a long neck	84
cranium	*noun* - part of the skull that protects the brain	28, 47, 48
cranky	*adjective* - grumpy; peculiar	31
cravat	*noun* - a piece of cloth worn around the neck, similar to a tie	33, 64
craving	*noun* - a strong desire for something (usually to eat)	51, 75
create	*verb* - design, make; originate	72
creek	*noun* - a small stream	4

154

Word	Definitions	Seen on Pages
cricket	*noun* - a small insect that makes noises by rubbing its legs together; a game played by two teams with a bat, ball and two wickets	126
crisp	*adjective* - cool, fresh and invigorating (weather); dry and brittle (substance); *noun* - fried wafer-thin potato slices eaten as a snack	110
crochet	*noun* - a type of knitting with yarn	21
crocus	*noun* - a small yellow, white or purple flower	81
crowd	*noun* - a large number of people gathered together; an audience; *verb* - fill a space or area almost completely; move too close to someone	66
crucial	*adjective* - extremely important; essential; necessary	120
cruel	*adjective* - wanting to cause pain or suffering; brutal; harsh	54
cue	*noun* - prompt; reminder; a long piece of wood used in a billiards game	94
cuff links	*noun* - jewellery used to tie together buttonholes on shirt cuffs	33
culottes	*noun* - calf length, wide leg trousers	33
cunning	*adjective* - crafty; sly; devious; noun - cleverness	46, 75
Curie	Marie Curie (1867-1934) French chemist and physicist	142
curiosity	*noun* - a strong interest to know or learn; an interesting or peculiar thing	100, 121
cursed	*adjective* - doomed; put under an evil spell	1
cymbal	*noun* - a percussion instrument; a round brass plate which is either struck against another one, or hit with a stick	44, 88
dahlia	*noun* - a ball-shaped flower with long, thin petals	81
dam	*noun* - a wall built across a river to stop the flow of water and change the water level	120
dank	*adjective* - cold, wet, and unpleasant	108
Darwin	Charles Darwin (1809-1882) naturalist, geologist and biologist	142
dash	*verb* - move quickly; strike or hit something with great force	124
date	*noun* - a day of the month or year; a social meeting or appointment; a partner with whom one has a date; verb - establish a date of an object or event; reveal as old-fashioned; go out with someone on a date	126
DaVinci	Leonardo daVinci (1452-1519) Italian painter, sculptor, architect and inventor	142
dawn	*noun* - beginning of daylight on a day	93
dearth	*noun* - lack (of something), scarcity	21, 93
debate	*noun* - a formal discussion with arguments on a topic presented; *verb* - to argue or have a debate	54
debrief	*verb* - interview or question someone about an activity that has taken place	26
decade	*noun* - ten years	120
decahedron	*noun* - a solid figure, with ten plane faces	65
decay	*verb* - cause to rot or decompose; fall into ruin	92
deceased	*adjective* - dead	114
deceitful	*adjective* - dishonest, untrustworthy	17, 69, 93
deceive	*verb* - mislead others; be intentionally dishonest for personal gain	106
deceptive	*adjective* - misleading	17, 22
decimate	*verb* - totally destroy	64
decline	*verb* - turn down, refuse; become smaller, fewer, or less powerful; *noun* – a gradual loss of strength or number	8
decorate	*verb* - make something more attractive by adding things to it; give an award or medal to someone	106
defect	*noun* - a fault; flaw; *verb* - abandon one's country and change nationality	72
deflated	*adjective* - feeling less confident; disappointed	59
defy	*verb* - refuse to obey; act against; challenge	98
dejected	*adjective* - sad and depressed; disappointed; miserable	15
delay	*verb* - make late, slow the progress of something	54, 96

Word	Definitions	Seen on Pages
delphinium	*noun* - a plant that has tall spikes of blue, pink, white, or purple flowers	81
delusion	*noun* - a mistaken belief, despite knowing it is probably not true	74
demolish	*verb* - destroy; ruin; tear down (a building)	20, 64
dense	*adjective* - thick, closed packed together	42
dent	*noun* - a dimple made on a surface; a reduction	42
depressed	*adjective* - sad and unhappy	15
desert	*noun* - a large area of dry land with little vegetation or water; *verb* - abandon; leave without permission	94
despise	*verb* - detest; hate	93
despondent	*adjective* - discouraged; disheartened; sad	15, 72
despot	*noun* - a tyrannical leader	69
dessert	*noun* - a sweet dish served at the end of a meal	94
detect	*verb* - become aware of; discover	74
dexterity	*noun* - the ability to use hands well to perform tasks	31
dictator	*noun* - a ruler who has total power	114
die	*verb* - stop living; become extinct; vanish; to be very keen for something; *noun* - singular form of dice; a shaped piece used to mould metal or plastic	94
dietician	*noun* - healthy eating expert	132
dice	*noun* - pair of small cubes (6-sided) numbered with dots, used in many games	94
dilapidated	*adjective* - old and broken down, in poor condition (usually of a house)	61
diluted	*adjective* - weakened by adding water or another solvent; made weaker	21
din	*noun* - a loud and prolonged noise	26
dinghy	*noun* - a small open boat	60
diplomatic	*adjective* - careful not to offend; concerning relationships between two countries	120
dire	*adjective* - dreadful; very serious or extreme	21
discourage	*verb* - cause to lose confidence and hope; dishearten; demoralise	63
discover	*verb* - find; become aware of; be the first to find or observe something	74
discus	*noun* - a disc thrown in an athletics sport	64, 69
discuss	*verb* - talk about	64
disguise	*verb* - change one's appearance, to hide their true identity; camouflage, conceal	57
dishevelled	*adjective* - messy; untidy	51
dismal	*adjective* - dull, dreary, gloomy; (of a performance) bad	100, 110
disobey	*verb* - break the rules	72
disposed	*adjective* - willing, or inclined to	103, 105
dispute	noun - argument	28
dissipate	*verb* - cause to gradually disappear; dissolve; become less	21
distance	*noun* - measurement of the length between two points; remoteness; far off; an interval of time; *verb* - withdraw or separate from someone; declare that one is not associated with someone else	80
distinct	*adjective* - clear; unique; physically separate; easily recognizable	77
distraught	*adjective* - desperately upset	93
donate	*verb* - give to a good cause; give blood or body organs to help save lives	54
donation	*noun* - gift, usually to a charity	26
dozen	*noun* - twelve	54
draughty	*adjective* - a place where air escapes and cools an area	110
dramatic	*adjective* - relating to the study of drama; sudden and striking; exciting; intended to create an effect	74
dreary	*adjective* - dull; dismal	110
drench	*verb* - make someone extremely wet (past tense - drenched)	108
dribble	*verb* - cause a liquid to flow in very small amounts; saliva escaping from the mouth; move a football along the ground	93

Word	Definitions	Seen on Pages
drizzle	*noun* - light rain	108
dromedary	*noun* - an Arabian camel that has one hump	4
drought	*noun* - a long period without rain, leading to a water shortage	112
dry	*adjective* - not moist or wet; having lost all moisture; with little or no rain; a subtle sense of humour	100, 108
dual	*adjective* - consisting of two parts	94
duck	*noun* - a water bird with short legs and webbed feet; *verb* - move your head down quickly	124
duel	*noun* - a formal fight between two people, to resolve an argument (historic); a competition between two sides	94
dull	*adjective* - not interesting; not bright, cloudy (weather); not sharp; *verb* - make something less severe	108
dusk	*noun* - the time that the sun goes down, when it is not yet dark	93, 114
dwelling	*noun* - a house, apartment, or other living space	64, 74
dwindle	*verb* - become fewer	89
easel	*noun* - frame use to hold canvas whilst a picture is being painted	31
ebb	*verb* - (of the tide) move away from land, out to sea; (of emotions) to diminish or decrease; *noun* - movement of the tide out to sea	92
ebony	*noun* - the colour black; black or dark brown wood from a type of tropical tree	1
economical	*adjective* - careful with money; inexpensive	51
economist	*noun* - an expert in the study of economics	132
economize	*verb* - spend less; use resources carefully to make them last longer	91
economy	*noun* - the state of something as it relates to production and money supply (usually a country or region); careful management of resources or money	132
Edison	Thomas Edison (1847-1931) American inventor (light bulb, phonograph)	141
effort	*noun* - a determined attempt; activity needed to achieve something	28
Eire	*noun* - Ireland (Irish term)	31
elderly	*adjective* - old or aging; *noun* - older people as a group	64
elegant	*adjective* - pleasing and graceful	100
elephantine	*adjective* - relating to elephants	120
elevated	*adjective* - raised	28
elliptical	*adjective* - oval	3,
elm	*noun* - type of deciduous tree	87
embark	*verb* - board a ship or aircraft; set off (usually on a journey)	78
embarrassment	*noun* - shame; humiliation; having more options, money or resources than necessary (embarrassment of riches)	38
embellish	*verb* - make a story sound better by exaggerating or adding detail which is often untrue; make something better by decorating or adding features	51
embezzle	*verb* - steal money from the company or organization one works for	91
emerald	*noun* - a bright green precious stone; a bright green colour	76
emulsion	*noun* - a mixture of a liquid with another liquid that does not dissolve; a type of paint used for walls	77
enchanting	*adjective* - charming; magical	51
enclosure	*noun* - an area surrounded by a barrier; a document or object placed together with a letter in an envelope	74
encouraging	*adjective* - giving support and confidence	63
encyclopedia	*noun* - book or set of books with facts on many subjects	33
endanger	*verb* - put someone at risk; jeopardise	93, 116
endure	*verb* - suffer patiently; cope with	116
engineer	*noun* - someone who designs, builds or maintains engines, machines or structures	132

Word	Definitions	Seen on Pages
enigma	*noun* - something mysterious and difficult to explain; a puzzle	69
enlighten	*verb* - make aware; advise, inform	57
entire	*adjective* - whole, complete, total	73
equator	*noun* - imaginary line around the centre of the globe	69
equine	*adjective* - related to horses	120
erratic	*adjective* - unpredictable in movement or action; unstable	63
errand	*noun* - a short journey for a particular purpose	114
escalate	*verb* - increase rapidly; soar; surge	20
escort	*noun* - person or group that accompanies another as protection; someone who accompanies another to an event; *verb* - accompany someone as an escort	100
essay	*noun* - a written composition	28
estate agent	*noun* - someone who sells, rents or manages homes and properties	132
esteem	*noun* - respect for someone	31, 77
estuary	*noun* - the mouth of a river, where it joins the sea	69, 114
ewe	*noun* - a female sheep	31, 42, 69
exaggerate	*verb* – say something is better or worse than it actually is; overstate	51
exasperated	*adjective* - extremely frustrated	15
excessive	*adjective* - too much	71, 75
exhale	*verb* - breathe out	69
exhaustive	*adjective* - considering all aspects; complete, comprehensive	73
exhilarating	*adjective* - very exciting	74
exorbitant	*adjective* - very expensive	75
expand	*verb* - become bigger	25
expel	*verb* - force out	28
expenditure	*noun* - money spent	20
exploit	*verb* - to take advantage of; benefit unfairly; noun - an adventure	69
expose	*verb* - uncover, reveal; make vulnerable; introduce someone to; reveal the true nature of someone or something; *noun* - (exposé) a report in the media that reveals something negative, such as a scandal	106
exquisite	*adjective* - very beautiful	47, 48
exterior	*adjective* - concerning the outside of something; noun - the outer surface of something	92
extinct	*adjective* - no longer in existence	133
extract	*verb* - remove, take out; force out; noun - a part taken out; selection	69
extravagant	*adjective* - spending or costing a lot of money	71, 75
fabrication	*noun* - a lie; process of manufacturing or inventing something	21
faint	*adjective* - light in colour; to lose consciousness for a time	28
fallow	*adjective* - left bare; unproductive	25
falter	*verb* - lose strength, hesitate, stall	21
familiar	*adjective* - well-known, recognisable; in close friendship	59
famished	*adjective* - very hungry	72, 75
farrier	*noun* - a person that provides shoes for horses	132
fatal	*adjective* - deadly	78
fathom	*noun* - a measure of depth (6 feet); *verb* - understand, comprehend	20
favour	*noun* - approval; preference or bias; an act of kindness; small gift given to party guests; *verb* - show preference for; recommend; give unfair preference to; be to the advantage of; accommodate, oblige	96
favourable	*adjective* - expressing approval; beneficial	75
feat	*noun* - an achievement requiring skill, courage or strength	94
feeble	*adjective* - weak, frail, puny	15
feet	*noun* - plural of foot	94

Word	Definitions	Seen on Pages
feline	*adjective* - relating to cats; *noun* - a cat	4, 120
ferment	*verb* - incite or cause (trouble); undergo fermentation (chemical process where a substance breaks down into a simpler substances)	21
fern	*noun* - green plant with a long stem and feathery leaves, and no flowers	76
fertile	*adjective* - able to produce vegetation or crops; able to have children	10
festive	*adjective* - relating to a festival, such as Christmas; cheerful, merry, joyous	15
fickle	*adjective* - easily changes sides or opinion	51
fiction	*noun* - type of story that is imaginative writing, not based on real people or facts; statements made that are false but presented as true	98
financial	*adjective* - regarding money	69
finch	*noun* - a type of colourful songbird that has a short, wide, pointed beak	84
fir	*noun* - a tall evergreen tree	87
firm	*adjective* - not soft but not completely hard; strong and tight; fixed in place or position; certain and not likely to change; forceful; *noun* - a company	124
flair	*noun* - talent to do something well; style and originality	126
flat	*adjective* - level, horizontal; lacking emotion, dull; depressed; fixed (of a price); *noun* - an apartment; the flat part of something	126
flaw	*noun* - a defect, or blemish; fault in someone's character; shortcoming; *verb* - degrade, or weaken something	78
flawless	*adjective* - without error, perfect	20
flea	*noun* - type of small insect that is a parasite on mammals and birds	94
flee	*verb* - leave quickly, usually to escape danger	94
flint	*noun* - a grey stone, often used to make tools	50, 114
flippant	*adjective* - not serious, trying to be funny; showing a disrespectful attitude	69
florist	*noun* - a store that sells flowers	34
flotilla	*noun* - a small fleet of ships (or boats)	4, 120
focus	*noun* - the centre of interest; hub; having well-defined vision; *verb* - see clearly; concentrate on	105, 120
foe	*noun* - enemy	28
foggy	*adjective* - hazy, misty; confused	108
foil	*noun* - a metallic sheet; *verb* - prevent something from happening	28
foliage	*noun* - leaves of a plant	4
forceps	*noun* - a pair of pincers used by a doctor in surgery	88
ford	*noun* - shallow part of a river; *verb* - cross a river at a shallow point	103, 105
forgery	*noun* - a copy or imitation of something, usually illegally	63
forgo	*verb* - do without	20
fort	*noun* - a strong building that keeps soldiers safe	4
fortuitous	*adjective* - happening by luck; fortunate	75
fortunate	*adjective* - lucky	10, 75, 92
foul	*adjective* - offensive; immoral, obscene; putrid, contaminated; wet and stormy (weather); *noun* - a violation of the rules in a game	40
foundry	*noun* - a factory for casting metal	4
foundation	*noun* - base of a building; a principle; justification; the act of creating something; an organization that distributes money or promotes research	54
fowl	*noun* - a bird, or collective term for birds	40, 100
frail	*adjective* - weak, fragile	59
frame	*noun* - a rigid form that surrounds something like a window or door; the supporting structure of an object; the structure that supports a system or idea; *verb* - mount a picture in a frame; form a plan	120
freesia	*noun* - an African plant with colourful, tubular flowers	81
freezing	*adjective* - below 0°C; icy	36

Word	Definitions	Seen on Pages
frequent	*adjective* - often; recurring; regular; *verb* - visit a place often	92
fret	*verb* - worry; be nervous	54, 96
frigid	*adjective* - very cold in temperature	36
furious	*adjective* - very angry, enraged, irate	47, 48
futile	*adjective* - useless; not capable of success	20
futon	*noun* - a couch than can transform into a bed	33
gain	*verb* - get, obtain, or acquire; *noun* - a profit or advantage	1
gait	*noun* - a way of walking	44
Galileo	Galileo Galilei (1564-1642) Italian astronomer	141
gallant	*adjective* - brave, courageous, valiant; courteous, gentlemanly	15, 114
galoshes	*noun* - rubber shoes to wear in a wet place	3
gargantuan	*adjective* - huge, very large	21
garnet	*noun* - a dark red precious stone; a dark red colour	76
gate	*noun* - a door in a wall or fence; an exit to board a plane in an airport	44
gauntlet	*noun* - a strong glove	21
gavel	*noun* - the 'hammer' used by a judge in court	20
gem	*noun* - a precious stone; something of outstanding quality	47, 48
genes	*noun* - (plural) hereditary cells passed down through generations	42
gent	*noun* - a gentleman	77
genuine	*adjective* - authentic; real; actual	63
geo (root)	earth	136, 138
geranium	*noun* - a common plant that has red, pink or white flowers	81
gifted	*adjective* - having an exceptional talent or ability	17, 75
gingerly	*adverb* - carefully	47, 48
glacial	*adjective* - made or left by a glacier; extremely cold (weather)	110
gladiolus	*noun* - a plant with a long stem and brightly coloured flowers	81
glazier	*noun* - a person that fits glass into windows and doors	132
globe	*noun* - the world; a ball-shaped object	66
gloomy	*adjective* - poorly-lit; dreary; causing depression; discouraged	110
glutton	*noun* - someone who eats and drinks too much	69
gold	*noun* - yellow precious metal, used to make jewellery and coins; a yellow or yellow-brown colour; something made of gold; something highly valued or treasured	76
gown	*noun* - a long dress	20, 33
granite	*noun* - very hard rock using in building	50
grant	*verb* - agree to, allow; give; admit something is true; *noun* - an amount of money given by a government or organization	89
graphite	*noun* - a dark grey form of carbon used in pencils	76
grasp	*verb* - take in your hands and hold tight; seize; understand	66
grave	*noun* - a place in the ground where a person is buried after death; *adjective* - serious; solemn	98
grey	*adjective* - a colour between black and white; having hair that has turned grey; weather when there are a lot of clouds	110
grieve	*verb* - feel sorrow following a death; mourn	69
grimace	*noun* - a pained expression on the face; scowl; *verb* - make a grimace	3, 26
gripe	*verb* - complain continuously; grumble; moan; *noun* - complaint	51
grotesque	*adjective* - ugly; repulsive	1
grouse	*noun* - a medium-sized wild bird with a plump body	84
gruesome	*adjective* - horrifying, hideous, frightful	20
guarantee	*noun* - promise; contract, warranty; *verb* - formally assure; make a promise	91
guillotine	*noun* - instrument used to behead people	50

Word	Definitions	Seen on Pages
guise	*noun* - an external appearance, that usually conceals the actual identity of someone or something	40
gullible	*adjective* - easily persuaded; too trusting of others	92
gusty	*adjective* - very windy	110
guy	*noun* - a man	40
Gutenberg	Johannes Gutenberg (1400-1468) inventor of the printing press	141
haberdashery	*noun* - small items used in sewing; a department that sells sewing items	20
haddock	*noun* - a fish from the North Atlantic Ocean	4, 33
hamper	*noun* - a basket used to carry food (especially for a picnic); verb - hinder; block	61
hapless	*adjective* - unlucky, unfortunate	8, 78
harp	*noun* - a large string instrument; *verb* - talk incessantly about something	94, 120
hastily	*adverb* - quickly	122
haughty	*adjective* - arrogant and acting superior to others	17
Hawking	Stephen Hawking (1942-2018) - Author of A Brief History of Time	142
hawthorn	*noun* - a type of shrub or tree of the rose family	87
hazel	*noun* - a small tree that produces edible nuts	87
hazy	*adjective* - unclear, vague; foggy; cloudy	63
heir	*noun* - a person in line to receive an estate or other fortune	26, 31
helix	*noun* - a spiral	4
hemp	*noun* - plant used for making rope, paper and fabrics	63
heron	*noun* - a large bird with long legs and a long neck, that lives near the water	84
hesitate	*verb* - pause before you say or do something; be reluctant to do something	78
hibiscus	*noun* - a tropical plant with large, colourful flowers	81
hickory	*noun* - a small tree from North America and East Asia, which produces pecans (nuts that can be eaten)	87
hidden	*adjective* - kept out of sight; concealed	63
hide	*verb* - conceal; stay out of sight	1
highway	*noun* - a main road, usually one that joins towns and cities	61
hinder	*verb* - block; get in the way; make something difficult to happen	9, 96
hive	*noun* - a place where bees live; the group of bees in a hive; a place of activity; a skin condition (hives)	120
hoard	*noun* - a store or collection of something of value; verb - accumulate items and hide them away	46
hoarse	*adjective* - having a rough voice (usually with a sore throat)	40
hoax	*noun* - a deception; a false story or trick done as a joke	63, 106
honest	*adjective* - truthful, sincere; genuine, authentic	93
horde	*noun* - crowd; large amount of people	66
horn-rimmed	*adjective* - a type of glasses with rims made of horn or tortoise shell	3
host	*noun* - person or group that receives and entertains others as guests; a television presenter; animal or plant on which a parasite lives; collective for angels	38, 120
hostile	*adjective* - unfriendly; aggressive; belligerent; opposed	31
hub	*noun* - centre; main part of something	53, 63
humble	*adjective* - not believing you are important; modest	1, 10
humid	*adjective* - hot and wet; weather containing moisture in the air	107, 108
hydrangea	*noun* - a type of bush that has plentiful flowers in round mounds	81
hyena	*noun* - a dog-like mammal found in Africa that hunts in groups	120
hyper (root)	over	136, 138
hypo (root)	under	136, 138
icy	*adjective* - freezing; zero degrees Celsius or below	36
idle	*adjective* - lazy; unemployed; not working or in use	26, 63
ignite	*verb* - light, cause to catch fire; provoke (an emotion or situation)	47, 48

Word	Definitions	Seen on Pages
ignore	*verb* - take no notice of	59
imagine	*verb* - visualise or form a concept of something; believe that something untrue is true; assume	74
immature	*adjective* - childish; not grown or fully developed	64
immense	*adjective* - very large	92
immerse	*verb* - put in water or another liquid; engage oneself fully in an activity	26
imp	*noun* - small, devilish creature	4
impatient	*adjective* - unprepared to wait; quickly irritated; restless	120
impede	*verb* - delay or prevent something from happening; hamper; obstruct	20
impertinent	*adjective* - rude; disrespectful	51
imply	*verb* - suggest; express an idea without stating it directly	69
import	*verb* - bring goods into a country from abroad; move data electronically on a computer	26
impoverished	*adjective* - very poor	72
impure	*adjective* - mixed with other substances	57
incessantly	*adverb* - without interruption, continuing	46
incision	*noun* - a cut in the skin made by a surgeon; the action of cutting something	64
inclement	*adjective* - weather that is unpleasant, cold or wet	36
incognito	*adjective/adverb* - going under a false name; having one's true identity disguised	78
increase	*verb* - make greater; get bigger; *noun* - a rise in size or number of something	93
index	*noun* - an alphabetical list; sign or measure of something; pointer; finger	38
indifferent	*adjective* - not concerned; uncaring; neither good or bad	51
indignant	*adjective* - shocked and angry about a perceived unfairness	121
indigo	*noun* - a dark colour between blue and purple; a tropical plant from which the indigo dye is obtained	76
indispensable	*adjective* - necessary; essential	69
indistinct	*adjective* - unclear	110
indolent	*adjective* - lazy, idle	17
indulge	*verb* - allow oneself to enjoy something; treat	118
industrious	*adjective* - hard working, diligent	17, 20
inept	*adjective* - without any skill; incompetent; incapable	63
infantile	*adjective* - childish	64, 114
inferno	*noun* - a large fire that is out of control	116
inflexible	*adjective* - stubborn; not yielding; rigid, stiff	47, 48
influence	*noun* - ability to have an effect or control something; *verb* - have influence on something; persuade	21
inheritance	*noun* - fortune received from a person upon their death	103, 105
innermost	*adjective* - closest to the centre; most private or intimate (thoughts or feelings)	63
inoculate	*verb* - vaccinate	133
inquire	*verb* - ask for information	98
inscribe	*verb* - write or carve words on an object (such as a plaque or trophy)	118
insult	*verb* - speak or treat with disrespect; offend; *noun* - an abusive remark; slur	11
insure	*verb* - protect with financial compensation in case of an accident or damage	118
intercept	*verb* - stop someone or something from reaching a destination; obstruct	98
internal	*adjective* - inside; occurring within	98
interrogate	*verb* - ask in a harsh way; formally question (a suspect or prisoner)	66
intersection	*noun* - a place where two lines cross; the crossing of two or more roads	61
interval	*noun* - break; period of time; space between two points	54
intrigue	*verb* - arouse curiosity or interest; *noun* - the making of a secret plan; a mysterious or fascinating quality	80
irate	*adjective* - angry; furious	15, 46

Word	Definitions	Seen on Pages
irritated	*adjective* - annoyed, frustrated	46
jagged	*adjective* - rough and uneven with sharp , pointed edges	75
jam	*verb* - pack tightly; force something into a space or position; become stuck; *noun* - an instance when something becomes stuck; a predicament or awkward situation; a sweet spread made from fruit and sugar	124
jasmine	*noun* - a climbing, flowering plant	81
jeans	*noun* - a pair of trousers made of denim or cotton	42
jeer	*verb* - ridicule; laugh unkindly; *noun* - a loud and rude remark	21
jester	*noun* - a joker (in medieval times a court jester); fool	1
jigsaw	*noun* - a picture mounted on wood or cardboard, that is cut into pieces and must be joined together; a mystery solved by piecing together bits of information; a type of electric saw with a thin blade	88
joker	*noun* - someone who make jokes; comic	1
jovial	*adjective* - good-humoured, cheerful, happy	15
junior	*adjective* - younger; for schoolchildren aged 7-11; lower in rank or status	64
juniper	*noun* - an evergreen bush with small fruits that are used in making medicine	87
keen	*adjective* - very interested; wanting to do something	63
kernel	*noun* - the inside of a nut, which can be eaten	94
key	*noun* - small metal piece that opens a lock; one of the buttons on a keyboard; a means to solving or achieving; a group of musical notes; adjective - of crucial importance; *verb* - input data on a keyboard	126
kidney	*noun* - one of a pair of organs in the body, that filter waste from the blood	64
kin	*noun* - someone's family and relatives; adjective - (of someone) related	98
kindle	*verb* - set a fire; begin to feel an emotion	26
knave	*noun* - a dishonest person; rascal; scoundrel	1
knead	*verb* - press and squeeze (bread, clay); massage	42
knit	*verb* - make a garment by tying together wool or yarn using knitting needles	64
knot	*noun* - tie tightly; a tangled mass; an unpleasant feeling of tension in the body; a measure of nautical speed; collective for toads	38
labyrinth	*noun* - a maze	54, 96
lack	*verb* - be without, or deficient in some way	40
lair	*noun* - an animal home; a secret den	31
lance	*noun* - a long pole weapon with a pointed steel end; *verb* - to cut open	87
lap	*noun* - area between the waist and knees when sitting; one circuit of a track during a race	124
larder	*noun* - pantry; storage place for food	87
lark	*noun* - a type of small songbird; a joke or prank	28, 84
launch	*verb* - set a boat in motion; fire a missile or spacecraft into the air; throw or pitch; begin an activity or enterprise	73
lavish	*adjective* - luxurious, rich, elaborate; *verb* - give something extravagantly	1, 71
lax	*adjective* - casual, not strict, not careful; relaxed	40
leaf	*noun* - flat, typically green with a stem, part of a tree; page of a book	50
leak	*noun* - the accidental release of a liquid or gas; disclosure of confidential information	40
least	*determiner* - smallest; *adverb* - less than anyone else	93
lecture	*noun* - an educational speech; a long, serious talk; scolding; *verb* - give a speech; talk seriously; reprimand	79
leek	*noun* - a vegetable from the onion family	40
leisurely	*adjective* - relaxed, acting with ease; *adverb* - without hurry	120
lens	*noun* - transparent material that alters the direction of light	120
leotard	*noun* - stretchy clothing used by dancers and for exercise	120

Word	Definitions	Seen on Pages
lethal	*adjective* - deadly	22
lethargic	*adjective* - very tired; slow moving	17
lexicon	*noun* - all of the words in a language	78
liable	*adjective* - responsible (by law)	20
light	*noun* - brightness that comes from the sun, a fire, device, etc.; a lamp or unit that provides lighting; a flame; *adjective* - not heavy; bright; pale; not serious; not intense or severe; *verb* - start a fire; make an area bright	126
lilac	*noun* - a bush or small tree with fragrant violet, pink or white flowers	81
limb	*noun* - arm, leg or wing	26, 64
limit	*noun* - the greatest amount allowed or possible; *verb* - control something to keep it at or below a certain amount or level	57, 106
lingering	*adjective* - lasting for a long time	104, 105
linguist	*noun* - a person that can speak several languages fluently	31
lithe	*adjective* - can move quickly and easily; graceful	69
litter	*noun* - rubbish; a group of babies born to an animal at the same time (kittens, puppies, etc.); straw used for bedding	38
liver	*noun* - a large organ in the body	64
livid	*adjective* - very angry, furious, irate	20, 104-105
lobe	*noun* - a low hanging part, especially of an ear	31
locket	*noun* - a small ornamental case often worn around the neck on a string	33
lodge	*noun* - a house used for activities or sports; a hotel; a beaver's den; *verb* - submit a claim or complaint; become embedded in place; rent an accommodation	25, 31
lodging	*noun* - temporary accommodation	74
lofty	*adjective* - tall, towering, soaring	3,
logo (root)	word; reason	136, 138
loot	*noun* - stolen money or valuables; *verb* - steal	39
loyalty	*noun* - a strong feeling of support	15, 93
lucid	*adjective* - clear, easy to understand	46, 120
ludicrous	*adjective* - foolish, absurd, ridiculous	13
lukewarm	*adjective* - a mild warm temperature	36
luminous	*adjective* - giving off light; bright or shiny	112
lush	*adjective* - rich, luxurious; (regarding plants) having healthy, green vegetation	71
lute	*noun* - a string instrument	39
luxurious	*adjective* - extremely comfortable and elegant, usually expensive	1
mace	*noun* - a club-like weapon with a spiked head	4
mahogany	*noun* - a dark red-brown wood from the mahogany tree; a dark red-brown colour	76
maim	*verb* - severely harm or injure causing permanent damage	20
maize	*noun* - plant that produces sweet corn	20, 64
major	*adjective* - of great importance; a type of musical scale; *noun* - a military rank	96
mal (root)	bad	136, 138
malady	*noun* - illness; disease	8, 26
malice	*noun* - desire to harm; nastiness; cruelty	8
malicious	*adjective* - intending to cause harm; spiteful; hostile; cruel	8, 17
manor	*noun* - a grand home	4
maple	*noun* - a type of large tree, used for timber or its sap in making syrup	87
manse	*noun* - a house provided for a priest or minister of a church	103, 105
martyr	*noun* - a person that dies for a cause that they believe in	25, 69
mask	*noun* - a covering for the face, for protection, disguise, or as part of a costume; *verb* - cover the face with a mask; conceal or hide; cover	73
match	*noun* - a competition; an equal or equivalent; a lookalike or replica; a marriage prospect; *verb* - to go together with; be equal; set against in competition	128

Word	Definitions	Seen on Pages
matted	*adjective* - tangled into a thick mass	3
mauve	*noun* - a light purple colour	76
maze	*noun* - a network of paths or passages in which it is confusing to get through	54
mayhem	*noun* - disorder; confusion; chaos	1
mean	*verb* - express an idea; intend, aim; involve; result in; *adjective* - unkind, nasty	130
meander	*verb* - bend; twist; wander; *noun* - a bend in a road or river; an aimless journey	47, 48
mend	*verb* - repair, fix, heal; improve	120
menacing	*adjective* - threatening	112
mentally	*adverb* - in one's mind	134
mere	*adjective* - only; considered a small number or less important	53
meteorologist	*noun* - a weather expert	31
methodical	*adjective* - orderly, well-organized	120
microscope	*noun* - an instrument used to observe very small objects	64
might	*verb* - past tense of may; used to ask permission; used to express a possibility; *noun* - power and strength	128
millennium	*noun* - one thousand years	120
milliner	*noun* - a person that makes and sells hats	132
mimic	*verb* - copy the way someone or something moves or speaks; resemble, imitate	63, 72
mind	*noun* - intelligence; memory; opinion; brain; thoughts; attention; *verb* – be bothered, annoyed; be concerned about; make sure (that); look after	130
miner	*noun* - a digger (often of coal or gold)	132
mingle	*verb* - mix together; engage with others socially	46
minister	*noun* - the head of a government department	20
minor	*adjective* - of lesser importance; small; insignificant; *noun* - someone under the legal age of responsibility	96
minority	*noun* - the smallest number or part of something	1
minute	*noun* - sixty seconds; *adjective* - very small	122
mirth	*noun* - amusement and laughter	20
mischief	*noun* - naughtiness; trouble caused by something; collective of mice	38
misty	*adjective* - foggy, cloudy; indistinct; (of a person) with tears in the eyes	110
moan	*noun* - a low sound made expressing pain or suffering; groan	51
modern	*adjective* - new, up-to-date; contemporary	54, 96
modest	*adjective* - humble, unpretentious, unassuming; a small or limited amount	1, 28
moisture	*noun* - water as vapour, or in droplets on a surface	75
moral	*adjective* - concerned with principles of right and wrong; ethical; *noun* – a lesson learned from a story or experience; standards of behaviour	26
morning	*noun* - the time between midnight and noon	44
morose	*adjective* - sad, ill-tempered	77
morph	*verb* - change, from one thing to another	80
Morse	Samuel Morse (1791-1872) - American painter and inventor, helped to invent the telegraph and a code system of communication using dots and dashes	142
motivate	*verb* - inspire; encourage; give someone a reason to do something	63
mourning	*noun* - a time of grief following the death of a loved one	44
muggy	*adjective* - unpleasantly warm and humid	112
mulberry	*noun* - a small tree that produces purple fruits; a purple colour	76
murder	*verb* - to intentionally kill someone; noun - a group of crows	38
murky	*adjective* - dark and gloomy; dirty (describing liquid); suspicious, questionable	110
nadir	*noun* - the lowest point; worst moment	93
narcissus	*noun*- a flower, similar to the daffodil	81
narrow	*adjective* - having a small width; limited; by a small margin; *verb* - become or make less wide	120

Word	Definitions	Seen on Pages
nauseous	*adjective* - sick; feeling the need to vomit	20
navy	*noun* - a dark blue colour; a fleet of ships; a branch of the military forces that operate at sea	76, 96
nebulous	*adjective* - foggy, hazy; vague, unclear	110
need	*verb* - require; be obligated to; *noun* - something important that is wanted or required	42
neon	*noun* - a chemical element; fluorescent light; an extremely bright colour	26
nest	*noun* - a structure made by a bird for laying eggs; a place where an animal lives; collective for vipers, hornets, scorpions, etc.	38
neutral	*adjective* - impartial, unbiased, not taking a side; inoffensive; pale	51
Newton	Sir Isaac Newton (1643-1727) English mathematician, astronomer, theologian, author and physicist	142
nib	*noun* - tip of a pen that distributes the ink	120
nimble	*adjective* - quick and light in movement; agile	15, 54, 96
nippy	*adjective* - chilly (weather); able to change speed and direction easily	36
noble	*adjective* - showing fine qualities, brave; having a high social rank by birth	28
non-committal	*adjective* - not expressing an opinion; evasive	106
nonentity	*noun* - someone or something of no importance	21
nonstop	*adjective* - done without any stops	57
notice	*noun* - attention, awareness; a notification or sign; *verb* - become aware of	31, 58
novel	*adjective* - new or unusual; *noun* - a long written story, book	46
novice	*noun* - a beginner	21, 51
nullify	*verb* - make of no use or value; invalidate; abolish	69
nylon	*noun* - a tough, lightweight, synthetic material; fabric made from nylon	63
oak	*noun* - a large tree commonly used for its timber in construction and furniture	87
oasis	*noun* - a fertile spot in a desert, where water is found	20
oath	*noun* - a promise; pledge	26
obscure	*adjective* - little seen or known about; unclear; *verb* - conceal; confuse	63
obtain	*verb* - get, acquire	72
obvious	*adjective* - clear, easily understood	91
ominous	*adjective* - threatening	63, 72
omit	*verb* - leave out	28, 31
opaque	*adjective* - not able to be seen through, not transparent	21, 51
opponent	*noun* - rival, adversary; someone who disagrees with an idea	98
oppressive	*adjective*- harsh; cruel; (of weather) humid, sultry	108
optimal	*adjective* - most favourable; best	28
optimistic	*adjective* - hopeful and confident about the future; positive	21
opulent	*adjective* - expensive, luxurious	71
orca	*noun* - a type of whale (killer whale)	20
orchestra	*noun* - group of musicians with many different types of instruments, led by a conductor; collective for crickets	38
orchid	*noun* - a type of plant with a distinctive flower	87
organ	*noun* - a part of the body that performs a specific function; a musical instrument that makes sounds by forcing air through pipes, typically used in a church	128
organise	*verb* - make arrangements for; put in order	120
original	*adjective* - existing from the beginning; authentic, genuine; innovative, creative; *noun* - the earliest form of a thing; individual, free spirit	93
originate	*verb* - begin; start; create	63
orthodontist	*noun* - an dental expert that can align teeth	69, 132
oust	*verb* - get rid of	25
overalls	*noun* - a piece of clothing covering legs and torso	3

Word	Definitions	Seen on Pages
overcast	*adjective* - cloudy	110
overpriced	*adjective* - too expensive	75
overjoyed	*adjective* - extremely happy	93
pachyderm	*noun* - a large animal with thick skin (elephant, hippopotamus, rhinoceros)	4
pack	*noun* - a group (collection of wolves); container; bag; *verb* - put together in something; fill; carry	38
pail	*noun* - a bucket	100
pair	*noun* - a set of two things	40
palindrome	*noun* - a word or phrase that reads the same when spelt forwards or backwards (example: madam)	20
palm	*noun* - inside part of the hand; a type of tree that grows in hot environments	130
panicked	(past tense of panic) *verb* - to feel frightened	106
pansy	*noun* - common garden plant which has many brightly coloured flowers	81
papyrus	*noun* - plant based material that the ancient Egyptians used to write on	50
paramedic	*noun* - a person who provides emergency medical care, usually from an ambulance	132
paramount	*adjective* - of most importance	93
parched	*adjective* - very dry; thirsty	112
parchment	*noun* - durable writing material, made from animal skin, used in medieval times	50
parliament	*noun* - the highest law-making body in the United Kingdom; a group of owls	38
partridge	*noun* - a wild bird with a round body and short tail	84
passive	*adjective* - not involved; not acting to influence or change a situation	56
Pasteur	Louis Pasteur (1822-1895) - scientist responsible for pasteurising process which kills bacteria in milk	142
patch	*noun* - a small material used to cover a weak or torn point; a piece of cloth sewn on clothing as a badge; a small area or part of something	64
patience	*noun* - willingness to wait without complaining	100
patient	*noun* - a person requiring assistance (usually at a hospital); adjective – being capable of waiting	120
patriot	*noun* - a person that is a great supporter of their country	15
patter	*noun* - a repeated light, tapping sound; speech or talk	100
pea soup	*noun* - a very thick fog; soup made from peas	110
peaceful	*adjective* - calm, restful, still, quiet; free from war or violence	1, 120
peak	*noun* - the pointed top of a mountain; the point of highest achievement or performance; *adjective* - at the highest level; *verb* - reach a highest point	4
pear	*noun* - a sweet fruit; the tree which bears the pear fruit	40
pedestrian	*noun* - someone who goes on foot, especially in an area where there are vehicles; *adjective* - normal, not exciting	60
pendant	*noun* - a piece of jewellery usually worn around the neck	33
penetrate	*verb* - to go into or through something	51
penultimate	*adjective* - second from last	31
peony	*noun* - a plant with large red, pink, or white flowers	33, 81
periphery	*noun* - the outer limits; the outside edge of something	63
perilous	*adjective* - dangerous	22
perimeter	*noun* - the outside edge of an area; boundary; border	51, 74
perish	*verb* - die; (regarding food) decay	8, 31
periwinkle	*noun* - a purple-blue colour; a plant that has purple-blue flowers	76
permit	*verb* - allow; *noun* - a document that gives permission	100
perpetuate	*verb* - continue indefinitely; keep going	46
perplexed	*adjective* - puzzled, confused	17, 74
persevere	*verb* - to keep trying	69
personal	*adjective* - belonging to or affecting a particular person; confidential	121

Word	Definitions	Seen on Pages
persuade	*verb* - talk someone into something, through reasoning or argument	1
perturbed	*adjective* - feeling bothered or worried	51
pester	*verb* - frequently annoy or bother, not leave alone	46
petroleum	*noun* - oil from the ground, which is used primarily as a fuel	69
pewter	*noun* - a grey metal made from tin; a silver-grey colour	76
pharmacist	*noun* - chemist, a person trained to handle and give out medicines in a pharmacy	132
pheasant	*noun* - a large bird with a round body and a long tail	84
phobia	*noun* - a fear of something	47, 48
phone (root)	sound	136, 138
photo (root)	light	136, 138
physician	*noun* - a medical doctor	132
piccolo	*noun* - a small flute	88
piercing	*adjective* - going through or into something; very cold (weather); loud and unpleasant (sound); *noun* - a hole in the body made to wear jewellery;	110
pigment	*noun* - a substance that gives something a colour	90
pine	*noun* - a type of evergreen tree; verb - to deeply miss someone or something	87
pipette	*noun* - a small tube for transferring liquid	88
pique	*noun* - a feeling of annoyance; verb - to stimulate (interest); feel irritated	69
pirouette	*noun* - the act of spinning on one foot, typically done by a ballet dancer	120
piscine	*adjective* - of or concerning fish	120
pitch	*noun* - the quality of a sound; steepness of a slope; a sports field; *verb* - throw; attempt to persuade someone to buy; put forward (an idea); set up a camp	73
pitcher	*noun* - a large jug; a person throwing	87
placid	*adjective* - calm; peaceful	21
plaice	*noun* - a fish with a flat, circular body	33
pleasant	*adjective* - enjoyable	112
plenty	*noun* - a large amount of something; prosperity	121
pliable	*adjective* - easily bent; flexible; easily influenced	98
pliers	*noun* - a tool used for grasping or pulling	33, 88
plodding	*adjective* - slow moving	104, 105
plover	*noun* - a short-billed wading bird that lives near the water	84
plumber	*noun* - a person who fits and repairs water pipes	132
plume	*noun* - a long, soft feather or arrangement of feathers; a long cloud of smoke	114
plunder	*verb* - steal goods using force; pillage, loot; noun - stolen goods	87
pod	*noun* - a long, flat pouch where the seeds of some plants (beans, peas) are found; a container attached to an aircraft or vehicle; a collection of whales or dolphins	38
poinsettia	*noun* - a plant with bright red leaves, popular as a house plant during Christmas	87
pointless	*adjective* - having no sense or purpose	63
poise	*noun* - gracefulness; behaviour that shows confidence; *verb* - be balanced; be ready to do something	78
polar	*adjective* - relating to the North or South poles	110
poly (root)	many	136, 138
poncho	*noun* - clothing made of a single piece of cloth, with an opening for the head, popular in South America	60
pool	*noun* - a small area of water; a swimming pool; a small amount of liquid on a surface; a group of people (e.g. typists); *verb* - collect money or another resource for a group	38
poplar	*noun* - a type of tall, fast-growing tree	87
porter	*noun* - a person paid to carry luggage and other loads	132
post	*prefix* - after; *noun* - a pole or stake; written content or an image published online; *verb* - display; announce	21

Word	Definitions	Seen on Pages
postpone	*verb* - leave until later; delay	21
praise	*verb* - compliment; express approval; *noun* - approval; admiration; devotion	93
precipitation	*noun* - rain, sleet or snow	21, 75
predicament	*noun* - problematic situation	106
preposterous	*adjective* - having no common sense; ridiculous; foolish	13
priceless	*adjective* - treasured; so valuable no price can be assigned	10
prickly	*adjective* - thorny; unfriendly, irritable; complicated	75
pride	*noun* - a feeling of satisfaction or worth due to one's achievements, or those of another; self-esteem; a group of lions	38, 128
primary	*adjective* - main, central; earliest in time or order; regarding education for children 5-10 years old	98
prime	*adjective* - most important; best quality; a number divisible only by 1 and itself	28
principal	*adjective* - most important; an amount invested or loaned; *noun* - the most important person or lead in a group; head of an institution	44
principle	*noun* - a fundamental truth; moral; guiding concept	44
private	*adjective* - personal; for one's use only; having no public role; *noun* - the lowest rank in the army	58
prodigy	*noun* - a highly gifted and talented young person	17
progress	*noun* - forward movement toward a destination; development; *verb* – move forward; develop	28
progression	*noun* - the act of moving forward; improving	93
prohibit	*verb* - not allow; stop	78, 120
promising	*adjective* - encouraging; hopeful; favourable	63
promote	*verb* - encourage; actively support	63
prompt	*verb* - cause, bring about; remind someone to say or do something	28
proper	*adjective* - genuine; actual; of the correct type	46
protrude	*verb* - stick out	51
public	*adjective* - about the people as a whole; done in open view; *noun* - people as a community	59
puffin	*noun* - a bird with a brightly-coloured beak that lives near the sea in the northern parts of the world	84
pulsate	*verb* - beat or move with a steady, strong rhythm; throb	21, 51
pulverise	*verb* - to beat or crush something into a powder; destroy	64
pun	*noun* - a joke made based on different meanings of words; wordplay	46
pungent	*adjective* - a strong smell	21
pupil	*noun* - schoolchild, student; the dark circular opening in the eye	130
purposeful	*adjective* - determined; resolved; steadfast	63
puzzle	*verb* - confuse, perplex; *noun* - a game to test knowledge or skills; a mystery	17, 74
qualm	*noun* - unease, doubt	114
quantity	*noun* - amount; number	100
quartz	*noun* - a hard (usually colourless) mineral	50
quay	*noun* - a long structure used to tie boats so they can be loaded or unloaded	120
query	*noun* - a question; *verb* - ask questions	66
queue	*noun* - a line for orderly waiting; *verb* - to stand or wait in a queue	94
quiver	*verb* - tremble or shake; *noun* - case used for holding arrows	38
rabble	*noun* - mob; an unruly group of people	66
radiant	*adjective* - bright; shiny; illuminated	13, 112
ragged	*adjective* - (of clothing) torn, ripped; having an irregular or uneven surface	104, 105
raging	*adjective* - angry, furious	112
raiment	*noun* - clothing, garments	33
raise	*verb* - to lift up; increase; collect (money); bring up (child)	40

Word	Definitions	Seen on Pages
ram	*noun* - a male sheep; a long, heavy pole used to break down doors; *verb* - push or hit with force	128
ramble	*verb* - walk, usually in the countryside; talk or write at length in a confused way	90
rare	*adjective* - uncommon; not occurring very often; unusually good, exceptional	59
rascal	*noun* - a mischievous person; devil; scoundrel	1
rate	*noun* - a measurement (of speed); a price charged; *verb* - evaluate; judge	31
ravenous	*adjective* - very hungry	75
raw	*adjective* - uncooked, not processed; a feeling of sensitivity, painful; very cold (weather)	36
ray	*noun* - a beam of light	40, 120
re-establish	*verb* - return something to its previous good condition or status	106
reach	*verb* - arrive somewhere; stretch out an arm in order to grab something; *noun* - the act of reaching out; measure of the effect or influence of something	80
real	*adjective* - actual; genuine, authentic	42
rebuke	*verb* - scold, reprimand, admonish	21
receptionist	*noun* - a person who greets visitors at work	132
rectify	*verb* - put right; correct; fix	46
reel	*noun* - a cylinder for winding thread around; *verb* - to wind; lose one's balance	42
reform	*verb* - make a positive change	31
refrain	*verb* - stop oneself from doing something; *noun* - a repeated line or lines in a song	106
regard	*verb* - consider or think of; look at; *noun* - consideration, care for something; respect; best wishes	59
regression	*noun* - return to a less developed state; a lessening of the severity of a disease	93
reign	*noun* - time spent ruling (kings and queens)	28
reject	*verb* - turn down; dismiss as unacceptable; *noun* - a failure	59
relate	*verb* - connect (with); be related by family or marriage; feel sympathy for; tell	69
release	*verb* - let go; allow to act freely	72
reliable	*adjective* - trustworthy, dependable	46
remark	*verb* - say something, make a comment; *noun* - something that you have said	121
remnants	*noun* - small pieces left over from a larger item (usually cloth or carpet)	33
renovate	*verb* - to fix and improve	64
renowned	*adjective* - well known; famous	72
replica	*noun* - a copy	93
replicate	*verb* - to copy or repeat something	114
rescue	*verb* - help someone out of a dangerous situation; *noun* - an act of rescuing	68
resemble	*verb* - look like, or be similar to something or someone	98
residence	*noun*- a home	74, 100
restrict	*verb* - limit	56
reveal	*verb* - to make known or show something, that had not been seen or known	106
revulsion	*noun* - a strong feeling of disgust	77
rhododendron	*noun* - a large bush with bright flowers	33
riddle	*noun* - a question that is tricky to figure out, and usually has a funny answer; something that is confusing and hard to solve; *verb* - to make holes in something; ask a riddle	74, 121
ridiculous	*adjective* - laughable; absurd, hilarious	57
rigid	*adjective* - inflexible, cannot be bent; not able to be persuaded or changed	114
roast	*verb* - to cook food in an oven or over a fire; criticise severely; *adjective* - (of food) having been cooked in an oven or over a fire; *noun* - a large piece of roasted meat	96
robust	*adjective* - strong and sturdy; durable; tough	59, 90

Word	Definitions	Seen on Pages
rock	*noun* - any of many types of solid minerals; boulder; stone; someone or something extremely strong or reliable; rock music; a gentle side to side movement; *verb* - move gently from side to side; play rock music	130
rogue	*noun* - a likeable scoundrel; *adjective* - behaving in ways not expected, dangerous	31
role	*noun* - a part played; function or position of something in a situation	44
roll	*verb* - move by turning over; move or turn on wheels; *noun* - a cylinder, tube; a throw or toss (dice); a small portion of bread; a list of names	44
rota	*noun* - a list of things that have to be done and the people who will do them	1
rotten	*adjective* - decaying, decomposing; dishonest, corrupt; bad, unpleasant	46
rough	*adjective* - uneven, not smooth; not gentle; violent; (of weather) stormy; (of a voice) harsh; not finished; not exact	59
row	*noun* - a number of thing or people in a straight line; a noisy argument; racket; din; *verb* - use oars to propel a boat; have a loud argument	128
rude	*adjective* - not polite; offensive; sudden and unpleasant	51
rumour	*noun* - talk or a report of uncertain truth; gossip	87
rupture	*verb* - cause something to break, tear, or split	120
rural	*adjective* - not of the town, but the countryside	51
rye	*noun* - a cereal plant used for making bread	44
sabotage	*verb* - deliberately destroy or damage; *noun* - the act of damaging deliberately	8
sabre	*noun* - a heavy sword with a curved blade	104, 105
sack	*noun* - a bag; *verb* - remove someone from a job; attack a city, causing great damage	31
salamander	*noun* - a small amphibian with soft skin	64
saline	*noun* - a liquid mixture of salt and water; adjective - containing salt	28
salvation	*noun* - preservation from harm; act of being saved	10
sanctuary	*noun* - a safe place; a nature reserve; a holy place	74
sandal	*noun* - type of shoe with straps that exposes the top of the foot	63
sanguine	*adjective* - optimistic, positive; noun - a reddish-brown colour	134
sapphire	*noun* - a precious stone, usually blue; a bright blue colour	76
saturated	*adjective* - completely filled (with water usually)	108
scalpel	*noun* - a sharp knife used to cut the skin during a medical operation	88
scar	*verb* - a mark left on the body after an injury has healed	79
scene	*noun* - a picture or view of a place or activity; a place where something happened; part of a play or film where the action stays in one place	60, 61, 62
scent	*noun* - something that can be smelt; a trail marked by an animal's smell	42
sceptical	*adjective* - having doubts; untrusting	72
scoff	*verb* - to laugh in a cruel way; ridicule; mock	114
scold	*verb* - chastise; tell off	9, 93
scope (root)	see	136, 138
scorch	*verb* - to burn; cause damage by heat	36
scrawny	*adjective* - thin and bony	92
scruffy	*adjective* - untidy; dirty	54
scythe	*noun* - tool used for cutting crops, a long curved blade fixed on a long pole	50
seal	*noun* - something used to join two things together; a piece of material (usually wax) with a design stamped on to it, that is attached to a document as a guarantee of authenticity; *verb* - fasten or close; apply a coating to keep liquid from penetrating it; conclude, secure; fix a seal to a document	130
sear	*verb* - to burn; apply sudden, intense heat (cooking)	36
secure	*verb* - fix something so it will stay in place; make safe; acquire; *adjective* - fixed, tight, solid; safe	73
seize	*verb* - to take hold or possession of something quickly; take something forcefully	66

Word	Definitions	Seen on Pages
seldom	*adjective* - rarely; not often	25
sensible	*adjective* - practical; responsible	57
serenade	*verb* - to sing romantically	47, 48
serenity	*noun* - peace, calm	69
sermon	*noun* - a speech about religion or other moral subject	69
sett	*noun* - a badger's home	120
sever	*verb* - cut off; break off	28
severe	*adjective* - serious; very intense	20, 25
shabby	*adjective* - in poor condition; neglected; old and untidy	54, 96
shake	*verb* - tremble, vibrate; move something up and down or side to side with rapid movements; upset the confidence of someone; *noun* - a milkshake	122
sham	*noun* - fake, fraud; *adjective* - false, pretend	26, 63
shambles	*noun* - a state of disorder; chaos; disorganization	87
shape	*noun* - the outside form or outline of something; a geometric figure (e.g. triangle); the original form of an object; a condition or state of something; *verb* - give shape or form to	3, 39, 65
shawl	*noun* - a large scarf worn over the shoulders	33, 100
shed	*noun* - small structure used for garden storage, keeping animals, or as a workshop; *verb* - allow something to fall off; discard; let go; give off (light)	128
shelter	*noun* - protection from danger or bad weather; a place of safety; cover; *verb* – to protect someone or something; secure	64
shifty	*adjective* - suspicious looking; devious, deceitful	3
shoot	*verb* - fire a weapon; move suddenly and rapidly; kick, throw, or hit a ball (in sports); film or photograph	44
shot put	*noun* - an athletics event that involves throwing a very heavy ball	64
shrivelled	*adjective* - has become smaller and is wrinkly	112
shroud	*noun* - cloth for wrapping a dead person at a funeral; something that covers or conceals; *verb* - cover something in order to hide it; wrap or cloak something	1
shun	*verb* - avoid all contact with someone; ignore; reject	54
sideboard	*noun* - a flat-topped piece of furniture with cupboards and drawers	33
Siberian	*adjective* - related to Siberia (a large, cold region of North Asia); *noun* – someone from Siberia	108
silence	*noun* - the absence of sound, quiet; verb - stop someone from speaking, or cause them to be silent	122
silk	*noun* - smooth cloth made from thread produced by silkworms	63
sizzling	*adjective* - very hot	36
sketch	*noun* - a rough drawing; a brief description; a short humorous play or performance	54, 96
skim	*verb* - remove something from a liquid surface; move quickly and lightly; read something quickly so as to note only the important points	100
slander	*verb* - to speak unfairly about someone, so that it damages their reputation; *noun* - making false statements about someone	106
slate	*noun* - dark grey hard stone; a list of candidates for election to an office	38, 76
sleek	*adjective* - smooth and shiny	91
sleet	*noun* - wet, partly melted falling snow	75
slovenly	*adjective* - untidy and dirty; careless, lazy	69
slumber	*noun* - sleep; verb - to sleep	106
smog	*noun* - a mixture of smoke, gasses and other pollutants that occurs in large cities, making the air difficult to breathe	110
snapdragon	*noun* - a garden plant with white, yellow, pink, or red flowers	81
snobby	*adjective* - showing respect and importance for social position and wealth, whilst looking down on others	17

172

Word	Definitions	Seen on Pages
snooty	*adjective* - showing disapproval toward others; self-important	17
solemn	*adjective* - serious; formal and dignified; sincere	98
solid	adjective - hard, firm; not liquid or gas; certain, reasonable, sound; noun – an object that is not a liquid or gas; a figure with three dimensions that is not flat	73
sombrero	*noun* - a wide-brimmed hat	4
sopping	*adjective* - very wet; saturated	108
soprano	*noun* - singer of high musical notes; a musical instrument with the highest pitch in its family	88
sound	*noun* - something you can hear; a water passage between two seas; *adjective* - in good condition; well-reasoned; *verb* - seem like something; make a noise	73, 120
sovereign	*noun* - ruler (king or queen); a British gold coin; *adjective* - having the highest or most supreme power	21
sow	*noun* - a female pig; *verb* - plant seeds; cause something undesirable	31
spectacles	*noun* - a pair of glasses	3
spectrum	*noun* - the entire range; used to classify something between two extreme points; a band of colours, like those in a rainbow	120
speech	*noun* - verbal communication; a style of speaking; a formal lecture or address given to an audience	121
spell	*verb* - write the letters of a word in the correct order; leads to; results in; *noun* - a short period of time; words used as a magical charm or enchantment; ability to control or influence people	130
sphere	*noun* - a solid, round figure; ball; *root word* - ball	66, 136, 138
spoil	*verb* - destroy or lessen the value or quality of something; ruin; (of food) becoming not good to eat; ruin the behaviour of someone (usually a child) by being too lenient or overindulgent; be overly eager to do something; *noun* - goods stolen or taken by force (spoils)	79
spinster	*noun* - an unmarried woman	1
spring	*verb* - jump, leap; originate from; *noun* - the season after winter and before summer; a coil (usually metal) that can be pressed down or pulled out but returns to its original shape, used to absorb movement; a leap forward; an area where water comes up from an underground source	128
spruce	*noun* - an evergreen tree, typically used as a Christmas tree; *verb* - make neat, fresh and tidy	87
spry	*adjective* - active and able to move quickly; lively	25
squabble	*verb* - argue over a trivial (not important) matter	46
squander	*verb* - waste or lose through carelessness	56
squash	*verb* - crush or squeeze something, until it becomes flat or changes shape; put an end to; *noun* - a sweet, concentrated liquid that is mixed with water to drink; an indoor game played with rackets and a ball; an edible gourd	130
squeal	*verb* - make a high-pitch noise or cry	46
squeamish	*adjective* - easily made to feel sick or disgusted	46
stable	*adjective* - sturdy, firmly fixed; not likely to change; *noun* - a place where horses are kept	63
staff	*noun* - the employees of an organization as a group; a stick or cane used for support whilst walking, as a weapon, or as a sign of authority; the five lines on which musical notes are written (stave); *verb* - provide the people who work for a company or organization	128
stallion	*noun* - an adult male horse	4
starving	*adjective* - suffering or dying from hunger	75
static	*adjective* - still, not moving; noun - crackling noise heard on a phone call, radio or other communication	69
steadfast	*adjective* - loyal, faithful, steady	26

Word	Definitions	Seen on Pages
stethoscope	*noun* - a medical instrument used to listen to the heart or breathing	88
stifling	*adjective* - very hot and uncomfortable; making one feel constrained	108
stiletto	*noun* - a type of shoe with a long, sharp heel	63
stimulating	*adjective* - causing interest or enthusiasm; exciting	74
stitch	*noun* - loop of thread made when sewing; a sharp pain; *verb* - make, mend or join using stiches	64
stick	*noun* - a long, thin piece of wood, that has fallen off or been cut from a tree; a long, thin piece of something; criticism or punishment; *verb* - push an object into or through something; thrust; extend out; set or place; adhere; be glued to; be fixed in a position and unable to move or be moved	130
stonemason	*noun* - a person that carves and builds with stone	132
strife	*noun* - conflict; violent or angry disagreement	120
strut	*verb* - walk confidently in a way to look important; *noun* - a strong supporting bar in a structure; a confident walk	20
sturdy	*adjective* - well built; firm; steady; strong	1
sub (root)	under	136, 138
subdued	*adjective* - quiet; depressed; restrained	69
subsequent	*adjective* - next; following	54
subsidiary	*adjective* - less important but related part of a whole; *noun* - a company controlled by another company	64
succeed	*verb* - achieve something; take a job after someone has left	96
successor	*noun* - the person or thing that comes after	26, 31
suede	*noun* - leather that uses the inside of the skin	69, 114
suffocating	*adjective* - causing difficulty in breathing	100
sugar-coat	*verb* - make something appear better than it actually is; deceive	56
sullen	*adjective* - grumpy, bad-tempered	98
sultry	*adjective* - hot and humid	36, 108
summit	*noun* - the very top; apex	25, 90, 93, 103, 105
support	*verb* - hold up, bear weight; help, assist; maintain, back up; noun – something that holds up weight (pillar, post); assistance that is provided; help	63
surplus	*adjective* - more than what is needed; noun- extra amount of something left over after all needs have been met	93
suspicion	*noun* - a feeling that something is likely or true; doubt, mistrust; a slight trace	106
suspicious	*adjective* - feeling that something is wrong; feeling doubt or mistrust	100
swallow	*verb* - food or drink passing down the throat; put up with, tolerate; believe, accept; restrain, hold back; overwhelm, engulf; *noun* - an act of swallowing; a small bird with a forked tail and long pointed wings	84
sweeping	*adjective* - extensive, vast; far-reaching; wide; blanket	73
sweltering	*adjective* - uncomfortably hot	36
swift	*adjective* - fast; noun - type of bird	22
swindle	*verb* - cheat or deceive someone in order to gain money or posessions	1
swollen	*adjective* - enlarged	58
symbol	*noun* - a mark or image with a meaning; a thing that represents something else	44
syn (root)	same	136, 138
synonym	*noun* - a word that has the same or almost the same meaning as another word	1
syringe	*noun* - a tube used for sucking liquid out or pushing liquid in, especially with a needle	88
tablet	*noun* - flat slab of stone; a pill; a type of small, flat, portable computer	21
taboo	*noun* - something not talked about as doing so is considered improper; *adjective* - something prohibited by custom; forbidden	69

Word	Definitions	Seen on Pages
tact	*noun* - a polite and kind way of talking or acting without making anyone upset	114
tactful	*adjective* - considerate, understanding; careful not to say or do anything that would make anyone upset or angry	120
tailor	*noun* - a person that makes, adjusts or repairs fitted clothes; *verb* - make something for a specific purpose or person; customise	132
talon	*noun* - a bird's claw	47, 48
tangerine	*noun* - a citrus fruit with an orange-red skin; an orange-red colour	76
tardy	*adjective* - late; behind schedule	46
tarmac	*noun* - material used for surfacing roads	25
tartan	*noun* - a pattern of checks and lines, or a wool cloth with a pattern, usually Scottish	33
tawny	*noun* - a light yellow-brown colour, like that of a lion	76
teak	*noun* - a type of tree found in India and Southeast Asia; hard wood from the Teak tree used in making ships and furniture	64
teal	*noun* - a small duck; a greenish-blue colour	76
temperate	*adjective* - mild (of weather); calm (of behaviour)	36
tempestuous	*adjective* - full of strong and violent emotions; very stormy	112
template	*noun* - a shape used as a pattern; something that is a model or guide to copy	21
temporary	*adjective* - lasting only a limited time	57
tepee	*noun* - a conical (cone shaped) tent	20, 64
tepid	*adjective* - slightly warm; showing little enthusiasm	26, 36
textile	*noun* - a type of cloth or fabric material	33, 134
theatre	*noun* - a place where plays are performed	21
threaten	*verb* - intimidate; endanger	72
thrilling	*adjective* - exciting; exhilarating	74
thwart	*verb* - prevent something from happening; foil	93
tidy	*adjective* - neat; in order; well groomed; considerable; *verb* - put in order; clear up	93
timpani	*noun* - kettle drums	88
tip	*verb* - move something so that one side is higher than the other; pour from a container; give an extra payment for good service; apply the end of something pointed with a liquid; *noun* - a useful piece of information; an payment for good service; the pointed end of something; a place where rubbish can be left	128
toil	*verb* - work extremely hard	25
tolerate	*verb* - allow something to happen, permit; accept or endure	98
tonic	*noun* - a healthy drink	25
top	*noun* - the highest part of something; a lid, cover or cap; the highest rank or position; a piece of clothing that covers the upper part of the body; *verb* - exceed, be more than; lead; cover; reach the top of	130
torrential	*adjective* - very heavy (rain)	106
torment	*verb* - tease; deliberately cause suffering	25, 56
torso	*noun* - the section of the human body, without the arms, legs, or head	20
tottering	*adjective* - moving unsteadily and with difficulty	104, 105
trance	*noun* - a condition where someone is not completely conscious and not in control of themselves	74
tranquil	*adjective* - peaceful, calm, still, quiet	1, 120
tranquility	*noun* - a state of being calm; restfulness	46
trawler	*noun* - a type of fishing boat	69
treacherous	*adjective* - disloyal, unfaithful; dangerous, unsafe	60
triangle	*noun* - a shape with three straight sides and three corners; a three-sided metal musical instrument	88
tribe	*noun* - a group of people who share the same language, culture and history; a large family or other group	120

Word	Definitions	Seen on Pages
trickle	*noun* - a small amount of dripping liquid; a very small number of people leaving or coming; *verb* - drip slowly in a thin line (of liquids); move somewhere slowly, in small numbers	96
trilby	*noun* - a type of hat made with felt and having a dented crown	64
trivial	*adjective* - of little importance	1
tropical	*adjective* - relating to the area of the earth near the Equator; very hot (weather)	36
trotter	*noun* - a pig's foot	1
trove	*noun* - store of valuable things	74
tuba	*noun* - a large brass instrument, of bass pitch	120
turbulent	*adjective* - unsettled; chaotic; (of air or water) rough and stormy	89, 112
twilight	*noun* - semi-darkness when the sun is just below the horizon; a period of decline	61
ugly	*adjective* - not attractive	1
umpire	*noun* - referee	20
undertaker	*noun* - the person that arranges funerals and burials	132
unearth	*verb* - discover something that was buried in the ground; discover through careful investigation	74
uni (root)	one	136, 138
unimportant	*adjective* - minor, not significant	1
university	*noun* - a high-level educational establishment	79
unkempt	*adjective* - untidy; messy	3, 93
unpalatable	*adjective* - bad tasting; not acceptable	47, 48
unravel	*verb* - become undone; untangle; fall apart; collapse; solve (a complicated problem)	98
unruly	*adjective* - disorderly; uncontrollable	98
untidy	*adjective* - messy; not in order; disorganised	51
upholstery	*noun* - cloth or textile used to cover furniture	33, 133
urban	*adjective* - of or in a city or town	51
urn	*noun* - a tall, round container; vase	20
vague	*adjective* - unclear; uncertain	63
vain	*adjective* - having a high opinion of one's own appearance or abilities; conceited	17, 46
valiant	*adjective* - brave, showing courage; heroic; courageous	15
vast	*adjective* - enormous, extensive	26
vat	*noun* - a large tank for holding liquid	87
ventilator	*noun* - a machine that helps you breathe by moving air into and out of the lungs	88
verandah (veranda)	*noun* - a raised area with a roof along the outside a house, on the ground floor	21
vertebrae	*noun* - the small bones that form the backbone	20
vice	*noun* - immoral behaviour; bad habit; tool used to hold an item in place; *prefix* - next or second in rank to	88
vicious	*adjective* - intentionally cruel and violent; brutal	17
violin	*noun* - a wooden musical instrument with four strings and played with a bow	88
villain	*noun* - evil character in a book, movie or play	21
viscose	*noun* - a smooth material that feels similar to silk	46
volatile	*adjective* - unstable; likely to change suddenly and unexpectedly, usually for the worse; a substance that will change easily into a gas	77
voluntary	*adjective* - done by choice	69
waddle	*verb* - walk with short, clumsy steps, moving the body from one side to another	100
waive	*verb* - give up, abandon; overlook or disregard	44
walnut	*noun* - an edible nut contained in a hard shell; the tree on which walnuts grow	87
warp	*verb* - bend or twist out of shape; distort, make abnormal	59
warren	*noun* - a series of connecting underground passages where rabbits live	120

Word	Definitions	Seen on Pages
wave	*verb* - greet with a hand gesture; instruct someone to move; *noun* - a moving, arched ridge of water; a sudden increase or surge; a hand gesture; curly hair	44
weaken	*verb* - make less strong, or effective	11, 58, 63
wealthy	*adjective* - having a great amount of money; rich; affluent	61
weary	*adjective* - tired; fed up with	72
whet	*verb* - sharpen a blade; stimulate, arouse interest or appetite (past tense – whetted)	75
wholesome	*adjective* - healthy; good	56
willow	*noun* - a type of tree with long, thin branches that hang down	87
windswept	*adjective* - exposed to strong winds; untidy hair after being blown by the wind	110
wing-back	*noun* - a type of armchair	33
wit	*noun* - cleverness; humour; a joker	25
wool	*noun* - the hair of usually a sheep, used to make yarn	63
worry	*verb* - feel anxious or troubled; annoy; disturb	51, 54
worthless	*adjective* - having no value or use	11
wrap	*verb* - to cover or surround something; *noun* - a material used to cover something; a loose garment worn around the body; a type of sandwich made using flat bread	73
wry	*adjective* - using dry humour; mocking; sarcastic	44
x-ray	*noun* - a photograph of the internal parts of something, usually the body	88
yew	*noun* - a type of coniferous tree, whose wood is used to make cabinets	42, 87
yield	*verb* - produce; give way to, surrender; noun - an amount produced	31
yoke	*noun* - a wooden collar for animals to pull a plough or cart; harness	44
yolk	*noun* - the yellow part of an egg	20, 44
zeal	*noun* - great energy and enthusiasm	31
zenith	*noun* - the highest point; time in which something is the most successful	98

Answer Key

Word Search, page 1

CHEAT = **SWINDLE**, UNLUCKY = **CURSED**, PERSUADE = **COAX**, GAIN = **BENEFIT**, UNIMPORTANT = **TRIVIAL**, UGLY = **GROTESQUE**, HIDE = **SHROUD**, MAYHEM = **CHAOS**, WELL BUILT = **STURDY**, MODEST = **HUMBLE**, SMALLER NUMBER = **MINORITY**, JOKER = **JESTER**, A LIST FOR "TAKING TURNS" = **ROTA**, BLACK = **EBONY**, PEACEFUL = **TRANQUIL**, A PIG'S FOOT = **TROTTER**, LUXURIOUS = **LAVISH**, RASCAL = **KNAVE**, AN UNMARRIED LADY = **SPINSTER**

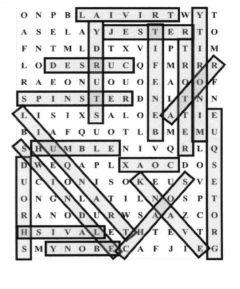

Where Am I?, page 4

HELIX – B2, FLOTILLA – C1, FOLIAGE – A5, TENT WITH AN AWNING – B1, FELINE – A2, PEAK – B6, PACHYDERM – C3, FOUNDRY – A1, AMPHIBIAN – C2, CREEK – A1, FORT – C5, HADDOCK – A3, MANOR – B2, IMP – C6, MACE – C4, SOMBRERO – C5, BOVINE – B1, CONSTABLE – A6, CANINE – A4, STALLION – C1, CHEVRON – B5.

The Dromedary is in B4. The two-humped camel in B3 is called a Bactrian Camel.

Spreading The Word, page 25

1) spry, 2) lodge, 3) oust, 4) toil, 5) seldom, 6) expand, 7) martyr, 8) summit, 9) wit, 10) fallow, 11) tepid, 12) import, 13) oath, 14) limb, 15) kindle, 16) sham, 17) vast, 18) immerse, 19) din, 20) malady, 21) astute, 22) grimace, 23) heir, 24) donation, 25) chord, 26) neon, 27) idle, 28) moral, 29) anchor, 30) debrief, 31) steadfast, 32) coy

Crossword, page 31

Shop 'Til You Drop!, page 33

Jazz's Jewellery: BROOCH, LOCKET, CUFF LINKS; Fred's Fashions: SHAWL, PENDANT, GOWN, CRAVAT, BERET, CULOTTES; Fishmonger: HADDOCK, PLAICE; Freda's Furniture: SIDEBOARD, PLIERS, UPHOLSTERED WING BACK, FUTON, BUREAU, ARMOIRE; Flo's Flowers: PEONY, RHODODDENDRON; Book Store: ANTHOLOGY, ENCYCLOPEDIA; Sew 'n' Sew: TARTAN, TEXTILES, REMNANTS

The Heat is On, page 35

Multiple answers, one suggested order : (Hottest to Coldest): scorching, searing, sizzling, sweltering, tropical, balmy, sultry, baking, close, temperate, clement, tepid, lukewarm, inclement, nippy, chilly, freezing, icy, bitter, frigid, raw, biting

Collecting Clues, page 38

army of ants; pack of wolves; pride of lions; pod of whales; litter of puppies; mischief of mice, murder of crows, ambush of tigers, nest of vipers, embarrassment of riches, host of angels, slate of candidates, orchestra of crickets, arsenal of guns, barrel of laughs, quiver of arrows, bed of oysters, parliament of owls, pool of typists, knot of toads, index of names, clutch of eggs

Dot – to – Dot, page 51

not transparent = opaque, desire = craving, neutral= indifferent, moan = gripe, worried = perturbed, exaggerate = embellish, careful with money = economical, outside edge = perimeter, untidy = dishevelled, magical = enchanting, a steady beat = pulsate, to go into = penetrate, difficult to carry = bulky, changeable personality = fickle, stick out = protrude, rude = impertinent, beginner = novice, not urban = rural, get faster = accelerate **Bonus Question**: PACHYDERM

Dial A Clue, page 53

DONATE = GIVE, DEBATE = TALK, INTERVAL = BREAK, AJAR = OPEN, SCRUFFY = SHABBY, CONTEMPORARY = MODERN, DELAYED = LATE, SKETCH = DRAW, FRET = WORRY, LABYRINTH = MAZE, AGILE = NIMBLE, AVOID = SHUN, FOUNDATION = BASE, SUBSEQUENT = NEXT, CRUEL = UNKIND, COMBINE = BLEND, DOZEN = TWELVE

Odd One Out, page 63

1) clarify 2) beret 3) capable 4) nylon 5) erratic 6) idle 7) originate 8) ominous 9) periphery 10) discourage 11) elderly 12) nail 13) limb 14) incision 15) salamander 16) renovate   17) television OR eye 18) discuss 19) cravat 20) teak 21) baguette 22) chief

Synonym Maze, page 73

commence > launch
launch > pitch
pitch > sound
sound > solid
solid > secure
secure > shelter
shelter > cover
cover > conceal
conceal > camouflage
camouflage > mask
mask > cloak
cloak > wrap
wrap > blanket
blanket > sweeping
sweeping > entire
entire > exhaustive
exhaustive > comprehensive
comprehensive > complete
complete > end

Colour Me Slowly, page 76

REDS: garnet, mahogany, blush; **BLUES:** teal, azure, sapphire, navy, indigo, periwinkle; **GREENS:** chartreuse, fern, emerald; **YELLOWS:** gold, blonde; **ORANGES:** tangerine, amber; **BROWNS:** brunette, tawny; **GREY:** graphite, pewter, slate; **PURPLE:** mauve, amethyst, mulberry

Hidden Link, page 79

1) Lecturer (UNIVERSITY) 2) Caution (CONSIDERATION) 3) Spoil (SCAR) 4) Adapt (MORPH)
5) Reach (DISTANCE) 6) Anonymous (INTRIGUE)

Floral Finds, page 81

A. GLADIOLUS, B. DELPHINIUM, C. FREESIA, D. DAHLIA, E. SNAPDRAGON,
F. CARNATION, G. AZAELIA, H. HYDRANGEA, I. JASMINE, J. CHRYSANTHEMUM,
K. BABY'S BREATH, L. NARCISSUS, M. PEONY, N. CROCUS, O. PANSY, P. LILAC,
Q. GERANIUM, R. HIBISCUS

Flights of Fancy, page 84
A.CRANE , B. FINCH , C. BUZZARD, D. LARK, E. PLOVER, F. HERON, G. ALBATROSS,
H. SWALLOW,   I. GROUSE,   J. PARTRIDGE

Hidden Amongst the Trees, page 87
The trees are: MAPLE, HICKORY, WILLOW, ASH, APPLE, CHERRY, POPLAR, ELM, SPRUCE,
FIR, BIRCH, BEECH, ALDER, HAWTHORN, WALNUT, JUNIPER, HAZEL, PINE, OAK, YEW

Being Instrumental, page 88
HOSPITAL: STETHOSCOPE, SCALPEL, FORCEPS, SYRINGE, PIPETTE, X-RAY,
VENTILATOR   CONCERT HALL: SOPRANO, BASSOON, CYMBALS, PICCOLO, TRIANGLE,
CASTANETS, VIOLIN, TIMPANI   FACTORY: VICE, JIGSAW, CHISEL, ANVIL, PLIERS

Missing Word Sentences, page 91
1) embezzled   2) economize   3) guarantee   4) sleek   5) ceased   6) obvious   7) chaotic   8) abandon
9) gullible 10) decay 11) adversity 12) ebb 13) exterior   14) frequent   15) caricatures   16) scrawny
17) fortunate 18) assembled 19) immense 20) casual

Fake News, page 93
1) original, deceitful 2) endangered, anxious 3) loyalty, admired 4) paramount 5) tidy, overjoyed 6)
thwarted, summit 7) praised, progression 8) surplus, dusk

Nonsense Poetry, page 94
Play on words: dual, duel; desert, dessert; cops, copse; flea, flee; bald, bawled; cue, queue; bow,
bough; colonel, kernel; feet, feat; palm; cordial; harp; die, dice

Quack Quack, page 100
1) brood 2) patience 3) shawl 4) skimmed 5) alighted 6) waddle 7) elegantly 8) bonnet 9) civil
10) dry 11) curiously 12) fowl 13) dismal 14) pails 15) residence 16) convenient 17) suffocating
18) quantity

Kidnapped Words! page 103
1)charge 2) disposed 3) summit 4) candidly 5) manse 6) ford 7) inheritance 8) tottering
9) bearings 10) lingering 11) sabres 12) plodding 13) ragged 14) livid

Colloquial Expressions, page 106
Lead up the garden path = COAX   Let the cat out of the bag = REVEAL
Get into hot water = PREDICAMENT   Smell a rat = SUSPICION
Mind your Ps & Qs = COURTESY   Hold one's tongue = REFRAIN
Sling mud = SLANDER   Have a feather in one's cap = DECORATED
Heart in your mouth = PANICKED   Take 40 winks = SLUMBER
Take the bull by the horns = CONFRONT   Pull the wool over someone's eyes = DECEIVE
Turn over a new leaf = RE-ESTABLISH   Sit on the fence = NONCOMMITAL
Pull someone's leg = HOAX   Blow one's own trumpet = BOAST
Raining cats and dogs = TORRENTIAL   Face the music = (BE) EXPOSED
Throw in the towel = CONCEDE   Draw the line = LIMIT

Whatever the Weather, page 107
COLD – bitter, brisk, crisp, dank, glacial, polar, Siberian; DRY – arid, drought, parched, shrivelled;
DULL – bleak, dismal, dreary, gloomy, grey, overcast; FOGGY – indistinct, murky, nebulous, pea
soup, smog; HOT – baked, stifling; HUMID – muggy, oppressive, sultry; RAINY/WET – dank,
dismal, dreary, drenched, drizzle, misty, saturated, sopping; SUNNY – beaming, brilliant, luminous,
piercing, pleasant, radiant; STORMY – menacing, raging, tempestuous, turbulent; WINDY – blustery,
draughty, gusty, windswept

What Was the Question? Page 114

Possible questions: 1. What is childish? 2. What are all breeds of dog? 3. What is the mouth of a large river? 4. What is a collection of hens? 5. What is the velvety inside of leather? 6. What is a witch's laugh? 7. What is a grey rock used for weapons and tools? 8. What is dead? 9. What is a long cloud of smoke? 10. What is to copy? 11. What is the opposite of dawn? 12. What is an uneasy feeling? 13. What is talking with consideration? 14. What is inflexible? 15. What is brave? 16. What is a ruler with total power? 17. What is a string of flags? 18. What is a short journey with a task? 19. What is help? 20. What is laughing in an unkind way?

Analogies, page 120

1) sound 2) flotilla 3) feline 4) fourteen 5) chatters 6) rays 7) prohibit 8) leisurely 9) break 10) comprehensible 11) light 12) narrow 13) dance 14) blue 15) millennium 16) sett 17) harp

Maddening Missing Letters, page 121

Words: plenty, indignantly, remarked, civil, invited, curiosity, speech, personal, riddles, aloud, hastily, thing, talking, conversation, minute, silence, shaking, fourth, angrily, butter

Professionally Speaking, page 132

Makes maps – CARTOGRAPHER
Studies the economy – ECONOMIST
Makes arrangements at a funeral – UNDERTAKER
Sells houses and property – ESTATE AGENT
Handles and carries luggage – PORTER
Doctor – PHYSICIAN
Greets clients at an office – RECEPTIONIST
Digs up and studies artefacts – ARCHAEOLOGIST
Fixes leaks – PLUMBER
Makes or sells women's hats – MILLINER
Designs machines or structures – ENGINEER
Designs buildings – ARCHITECT
Helps to straighten teeth – ORTHODONTIST
Provides emergency medical care – PARAMEDIC
Practises law in a court – BARRISTER
Makes and repairs clothing – TAILOR
Dispenses medicine – PHARMACIST
Fits glass into windows and doors – GLAZIER
Makes and repairs things in iron – BLACKSMITH
Cuts, prepares and builds with stone – STONEMASON
Makes and repairs wooden objects – CARPENTER
Expert on diet and nutrition – DIETICIAN
Works in a mine – MINER
Makes shoes for horses – FARRIER

You're Breaking Up, page 133

Answers: CACOPHONY, UPHOLSTERY, CATALOGUE, INNOCULATE, BAROMETER, EXTINCT, TEXTILES, COPYRIGHT, BOUYANT, MENTALLY, SANGUINE

Famous Anagrams, page 141

1) GALILEO 2) BABBAGE 3) GUTENBERG 4) EDISON 5) HAWKING 6) DA VINCI
7) BRAILLE 8) PASTEUR 9) NEWTON 10) CURIE 11) MORSE 12) DARWIN

Also available from the Armadillo's Pillow

The Big 11+ Logic Puzzle Challenge

- A unique collection of logic puzzles to challenge and prepare children for the Eleven Plus as well as Independent School exams.
- Includes: Non-verbal reasoning, verbal reasoning, riddles and brain teasers, worded problems, spatial reasoning, cube nets, mazes and much more!
- The variety of challenges should stimulate and keep children interested as they improve their ability to solve different types of problems.

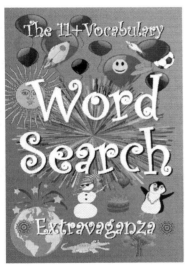

The 11+ Vocabulary Word Search

- Word Search book focused exclusively on vocabulary required for Eleven Plus exams
- Organised by synonyms, antonyms, subjects and themes
- Increase vocabulary retention and spelling through challenging word search puzzles
- Great companion book to *The Big 11+ Vocabulary Play Book*

The Big 11+ Maths Play Book

- 47 engaging activities, including games, puzzles, cartoons, and exercises that address key 11+ Maths subject areas in a lively way.
- A wide variety of activities make learning fun, resulting in improved results.
- A review section with over 300 questions
- Answer Key and glossary of Eleven Plus Maths concepts included

Contact us at: thearmadillospillow@gmail.com